Bernard J. Canning.

Feast of St. Albert the Gt.
15th Nov. 55.

A. M. + D. G.

THE PROBLEM OF ONANISM

By the same author :

DIFFICULTIES IN LIFE

DIFFICULTIES IN SEX EDUCATION

DIFFICULTIES IN MARRIED LIFE

The Problem of Onanism

By

BARON FREDERICK VON GAGERN, M.D.

Translated from the German by
MEYRICK BOOTH, Ph.D. (Jena)

MCMLV
THE MERCIER PRESS LIMITED
CORK

First published in English, January, 1955, by the Mercier Press, Ltd., Cork
Ireland.

Published in Germany in 1952 under the title *Die Zeit der Geschlechtlichen Reife*
by Verlag Josef Knecht, Frankfurt-am-Main.

Nihil Obstat :   Edward A. Cerny, S.S., D.D., *Censor Librorum.*

Imprimatur :   ✠ Francis P. Keough, D.D., *Archbishop of Baltimore.*

The *Nihil Obstat* and *Imprimatur* are official declarations that a book or pamphlet is free of
doctrinal and moral error. No implication is contained therein that those who have granted
the *Nihil Obstat* and *Imprimatur* agree with the opinions expressed.

Printed in the Republic of Ireland by
THE EAGLE PRINTING COMPANY, LIMITED, CORK

CONTENTS

INTRODUCTORY

THE QUESTION OF NEUROSIS

MANY WHO read my earlier books were surprised to find pen-pictures of themselves amongst the cases described. Very often these readers suffered a severe shock when they were forced to realise that traits in their own characters were, in reality, faults or shortcomings of a neurotic type: they had hitherto been convinced of their own rectitude, and now judgment was passed upon them. The more courageous amongst them heard the call to reformation and made a sincere effort, but those with less spirit felt deeply discouraged. Is it not useless to struggle against such serious faults ? they asked. Can we ever correct all that we now know to be wrong ? Shall we not be stamped as inferior men and women and as failures ?

This is a standpoint as erroneous as it is common. Human nature is weak, and despite every effort will never be immune from failure. We must all of us learn to play the game, to be good losers, to smile, even while we deplore our weaknesses, and to be patient with the frailties of our nature. We are lonely strugglers dependent upon the grace of God. Let us reconcile ourselves to the fact that we are all travellers and that none of us has arrived at the goal of perfection. This is to accept the human lot with faith and courage.

But must one not feel ashamed to realise that one is a neurotic or even, as it may be mistakenly said, a psychopath ? In the following pages, a number of factors will be brought into prominence which will certainly convince many readers that they do really show neurotic tendencies: for this reason I am anxious to avoid causing distress upon this point. The great majority of people, if they examined themselves, would be compelled to recognise that they have, in one point or another, failed to transcend puberty, or that, under certain circumstances, they revert to symptoms of puberty. " Men of genius experience puberty again and again ; other people are young only once," said Goethe, speaking from his own experience. This great man manifested symptoms of puberty at periodic intervals during the whole of his life. These took the form of, for example, enthusiastic romantic attachments to women, often to several within a brief period ; passionate mental excitement, the echo of which comes down to us in many poems ; feverish rest-lessness, such as that which took him, in the autumn of 1786, to the carefree atmosphere of Italy for two years, in the very middle of a work he had begun and without even saying goodbye to his friends ; ecstatic eagerness on the part of a man otherwise so calm and level-headed ; the " dreams of a councillor " which visited the 74-year-old man in Marienbad and Karlsbad, when he fell in love with

Ulrike von Levetzow, and the Grand Duke himself acted as his emissary in requesting her hand. All these and many other things are witnesses of a recurrent puberty which we cannot describe otherwise than as regression, as a failure to transcend puberty and attain to true maturity.

It may seem impertinent to bring forward Goethe, of all people, as an example of immaturity. Yet all the deep respect that we have for him cannot hide the fact that his character exhibited neurotic traits. Nor can we overlook a history of neurosis in the family. The doctor who reads Goethe's letters is compelled to perceive that they contain a wealth of material illustrating neurotic reactions and psychogenetic disease. He will not be surprised at the conclusions reached by Ernest Michel, who made it clear that Goethe's religious beliefs were of a neurotic and unreal character. He had no confidence in the historical truth of salvation and remained fixed at the level of belief in creation. If, in our analysis, we do not stop short of criticising even the greatest of poets, if we are compelled to find in his writings and sayings innumerable factors which indicate neurosis, it is not because we wish to belittle him. On the contrary, we would not detract in any way from his stature as a giant of the mind. He remains the Olympian despite his neurosis, just as we are forced to recognise neurotic elements in the lives of many of the great saints, who nevertheless *were* saints.

What can we learn from all this ? In the first place, that it is false to look upon a man who suffers from neurotic disorder as being *inferior* on that account—even when this man happens to be oneself. We must reject a dangerous error of the materialists who presume to pass judgment upon their fellow men. What they perceive is the utility value of a man, while the Christian has higher values whose measure is from God. Least of all when there is a question of neurosis dare we pretend to judge. That is the time to remember the words : " Judge not that ye may not be judged ! " As C. G. Jung said: " Everybody has some taint of neurosis." And who knows what the cause may be ? Disposition, environment, education—or, perhaps, some personal fault ?

We can go a step further and ask the pertinent question: are there any men of genius free from neurosis ? Now we begin to realise that there is no question of regarding neurosis as a characteristic of inferiority, for it can very well be a sign of superiority, of a creative power striving towards expression. Neurosis remains, however, a disorder. In the course of his life's journey, a man has to pass through three critical stages: the transition from pre-puberty to puberty ; the development leading from puberty to mature, responsible manhood ; and the period of growing old. Many fail to negotiate these successfully. They cannot travel onward, leaving the past behind them. They remain, in varying degrees, in stages that they should have transcended. Many *never* attain to full maturity.

Part I

SETTING THE STAGE FOR ADULTHOOD

WE HAVE all, at one time or another, come into contact with lonely people who refuse human ties : crusty bachelors proud of being woman haters, or withered old maids of both sexes. Such as these are confident in their supposed self-sufficiency—until one day they wake up to find themselves growing old in unbearable loneliness. These are the types who, even when married, are incapable of giving warm and wholehearted love. They have never developed to the point when they could expand in unselfish love for others. They have, in short, failed to reach full maturity. They never cease to make demands upon life. They give nothing. They grumble about life, about their hard lot and, even about God. Again, we all know the type who is *against* everything: the enemy of all established values, the man who cries " No ! " and is , at the same time, the fanatical advocate of " freedom at any price." Any sort of tie binding him to absolute values is like a red flag to a bull. Without realising it, such a man is the first to fall victim to the materialistic dogma of determinism, of no freedom for anyone. He seldom grasps the fact that he is not an individualist or a free man, but a cog in the vast machinery of the " masses," robbed of every opportunity of making his own decisions, a mere tool in the hands of the clever and unscrupulous demagogues of the day. Of apparently quite different mettle, and yet fundamentally similar, is the man who has no views of his own, who is always ready to submit to established authority: the patient, obedient, civil servant type, avoiding responsibility, afraid of decision and lacking in courage. In the same category we may place a man of my acquaintance who, although forty years old and married, was wholly dependent upon his mother for even the smallest decision.

To the psychologist who penetrates the surface of life and knows the stages of human development, it is obvious that all such types have never really transcended the phase of puberty. Their mental age is somewhat less than thirteen or fourteen. In the ranks of these under-developed men and women we find the unrealistic idealists, living in a world of their own, incapable of coping with the hard realities of life : day-dreamers, wish-addicts, dwellers in the clouds. We find also the Don Juan type, the man who is for ever chasing his own erotic images, thinking himself a " great fellow," little knowing that he is a pathetic figure caught up in the vicious circle of his neurotic mentality. Puberty is like a door ; one passes through and finds oneself in a larger room with increased possibil- ities. But there are many who never get through because they fail to develop and to qualify for participation in the fuller life awaiting them.

It is, however, true that some of those who fail to achieve an all-round development may prove to be geniuses in special fields, and may develop far beyond the normal as, for example, artists, writers, explorers, singers, or economists. The tangled personality of a man or woman whose general development has been arrested, may be compared to a cable in which some of the strands are sound, while others have unravelled themselves into a knot. However gifted such types may be, they cannot develop their whole power, unless their knots are straightened out, and they are thus enabled to become complete personalities. In almost every individual it is possible to discover elements that have not developed fully. Under the stress of illness or discouragement, we all tend to regress to earlier and easier stages of life. This sort of escapism has been dealt with in an earlier study in this series : *Difficulties in Life.*

The following study is justified by the many difficulties and complications which attend the passage from puberty to maturity, and indeed the whole period of adolescence. This is for so many young people a time of suffering when they stand in peculiar need of advice and aid. It is a fact of experience that parents, spiritual advisers, and teachers are too often devoid of any real understanding of the problems involved, more especially when it is a question of sexual matters. It is hoped that this little book may also be of some help to adults who realise that their own development has left much to be desired and who now wish to make up for lost ground. Their eyes may possibly be opened to signs of regression or escapism. Such dangers do not announce themselves ; one must track them down and attack them. It has not been possible to consider in detail the many problems falling within the range of such a study. It is my aim to present a selection of those factors which medical practice shows to be of significance to young people and their parents. Much of what is said may have been said before, but it is unfortunately the case that large numbers of parents and educators are ill-informed on these problems.

PHASES OF PUBERTY

IN SPEAKING of puberty, we are to be understood as referring to the period of development lying between childhood and early maturity ; say from eleven years up to about sixteen. It signifies not only maturity of the sexual organism but of the personality as a whole. Psychologists recognise more than one phase in this period.

There is apt to be a keen interest in everything to do with sex, and curiosity about the why and wherefore of differences between the sexes. With this, there is a tendency to increased independence of mind and action, with, in many cases, obstinacy and defiance. It must always be remembered that sexual curiosity at this time is not unhealthy or unnatural. Quite the reverse. It is a necessary phase of development, and it is the duty of parents to give satisfactory answers to questions. This is so important that we have devoted a whole book to sex education.* Evasion and silence are full of danger. Cowardice and lies on the part of parents indicate not only a lack of understanding but even a failure in the duty of parental affection.

The time of actual maturity varies greatly with climate and race. It is much earlier in hot countries. In Africa, the average age when procreation and conception become possible is about nine years. It is a sign of our age that children reach maturity sooner than they did in previous generations. At the same time mental and spiritual maturity is apt to be later, for reasons which are not clearly known. This discrepancy is probably related to the question of *security*. It is, at any rate, certain that the children of earlier generations were nurtured in a sheltered atmosphere altogether different from that of our day, with its dangers, fears and problems.

Before 1914, all seemed ordered and settled. To-day, millions have been shattered by the havoc of war, and the long years of nervous strain. It was then easy for a child to remain a child, untroubled by its surroundings. Now large masses of people live deprived of safety and order, their lives overshadowed by fear for the future, terror of atom-bombs and still more terrible conflicts. Worst of all, they have no faith in God or hope for the future. In Europe, millions have been uprooted, torn away from their homes, transplanted into alien and often hostile surroundings, their families scattered to the four winds. How can we suppose that all this can fail to leave a deep mark on the sensitive mind of childhood? It strikes at the roots of child life and stimulates an unhealthy, because premature, development of the physical and sexual. The necessary and complementary development of mental and moral powers does not, under these conditions, keep pace with the physical and the sexual. It is thrust into the background, with consequences of a highly deleterious nature. Consider such a half-mature youth. He is overwhelmed by the power of the newly awakened life of instinct, and is bound to look upon it as the dominating factor in life. By its side the world of the good and beautiful,

* *Difficulties in Sex Education*, by Baron Frederick von Gagern (*Mercier Press*).

which should lend wings to his young imagination and inspire him with idealistic—but not yet physical—love, appears of completely secondary significance, if not wholly meaningless. He is filled with an overwhelming sense of his own importance as a man already able to appear desirable in the eyes of young women. His eogism is enlarged beyond all bounds, especially if he has at home little of the love for which his nature yearns, and which engenders respect and real encouragement. When the sphere of sex is thus placed at the top of the scale of values, in a position far above all that is mental and spiritual, it tends to become all-powerful and is no longer held within the bounds prescribed by the hierarchy of soul over body. The unity of the individual, compounded as he is of both body and soul, is destroyed. The soul is not strong enough to take up its right position of command over the body, and to assign to the body its proper role as expression and revelation of the spirit. The result is a split in the personality, the degradation of the body to a vehicle of animality, and the failure of the sexual to attain to its true human function. After this defeat of the mental and moral forces, the mind creates for itself a new world of false values, and the individual drifts either towards nihilism or the anarchy of the purely physical.

The maturity of the soul, of which we have spoken, must not be regarded as synonymous with mental maturity, as is seen very clearly in the case of Goethe. The young people of to-day are often more developed *mentally* than those of the last generation. Yet they are not *mature*, in the sense of being capable of wholehearted love, unselfish devotion and positive faith.

This backwardness in the evolution of the spiritual nature may very well be connected with the early bodily maturity, which absorbs too large a share of the vital forces at the disposal of the adolescent. Another reason is, perhaps, to be found in a species of escapism: there is a feeling of fear at the prospect of facing the responsibilities and risks of adult life, and it seems safer, despite outward self-assertion, to remain on a more childish level ; in other words, it is a symptom of regression, of a desire to return to a stage that should have been transcended.

Finally, we would suggest that the foregoing situation may result from the widely prevalent lack of the warm and encouraging love that every child rightly expects from his mother and now needs more than ever to compensate him to some extent for the general atmosphere of anxiety and unsettlement. Unfortunately the mother of to-day is too often herself harassed and exhausted by the conditions of modern life. The child, lacking the needful warmth and encouragement, will use all his resources of defiance and cunning to remain wrapped up in his childish state and may develop an infantile neurosis. He will be apt to present his justifiable childish demand for love as an unpaid bill to be settled in the future, and accordingly he will fail to develop beyond the early stage of dependence on the mother. Growth beyond this stage is of decisive importance in the process of becoming mature. It is, of course, possible that all the factors we have mentioned work together in delaying spiritual maturity.

PRE-PUBERTY

THE FIRST indications of maturity are found in the years preceding puberty itself. Maturity of the whole being, body and soul, does not take place over-night ; it is being prepared gradually for many years before the crisis which brings it about.

The World of Dreams

During childhood, the world of reality and the world of dreams are both absorbed by the budding soul and become intermingled. But later, in the time preceding puberty, there is a conscious separation of the two. In the course of normal development, the world of dreams and imagination fades more and more into the background to make way for a realistic apprehension of the surrounding world, and the child emerges from his strange little realm of phantasy and fairy-tales. Even at this early stage, disturbances are apt to occur. If the instinctive urges suffer inhibition as a result of unsettled conditions and anxieties in the subconscious mind, the child is discouraged and does not venture to embark upon the exploration of the world of reality. He wants to cling to his old childish ways. He builds up a little dream world of his own in which he lives a substitute-life, although he may know that this is no longer appropriate to his actual age. Even if he does not know this consciously, a feeling of guilt may arise in the depth of his mind. The more he loses himself in the child world, the more he remains in the debt of the real world, and this feeling of guilt drives the child into a still greater isolation and state of discouragement until his condition is such that he is in urgent need of all the help we can give him.

We all know these children who wander through every-day life lost in their dreams, who seems to come from some remote place when called ; the quiet ones who live for themselves, and take no part in the life going on round them. Our attitude towards such children is often wrong. They are not, as many parents may think, naughty ; they are in need of moral and spiritual aid. They need love, patience and encouragement, and the feeling that we have confidence in them. We should give them little jobs to do, taking care to bestow praise freely, and encourage them to take part in the pastimes of their companions—even by taking part ourselves if it will help them. We must not forget that their little souls are ill, that their condition is to be taken seriously, and that it is our duty to strengthen their self-confidence, to help them to break out of their stagnation and take up the battle of life that lies ahead.

We have gained a lot if we have succeeded in so winning the confidence of a child that he will allow us to share his world of dreams. It is not our business to judge or patronise but to act as good comrades full of understanding, letting the child see that we too have had our day of dreams. This will make it possible for us to recognise what is false in the child's inner life and secret desires, and, when opportunity offers, we shall be able to correct the child or help him towards fulfilment. Perhaps we can open his eyes to the unreality of his world of imagination and afford him a glimpse of the possibilities and attractions of the real world. It will then be a necessary and rewarding task to place the child's feet firmly on the road leading to life.

A boy of eleven had completely lost himself in a magnificent Wild West phantasy which dominated every aspect of his life. His sole desire was to wander with lasso and gun through boundless forests, and spend his life far away from other people—in his eyes " bad " people. He was the most backward boy in his school ; but to be the very worst is after all something ! Everything in his world tended to discourage him completely ; he found no peace or security in the love of his unemotional and unresponsive mother, who afforded him no shelter either from the dangers in himself or those in the outer world. His mother admitted herself that she could not provide him with the affection he needed. " We do not seem able to get into contact," she said. " Each of us seeks something from the other."

In such a case, the attitude of the mother certainly needs to be reformed ; but, at the same time, it will be possible to make use oɪ the child's passionate interest in the wild as an enticement to bring him into contact with the open air life of some group, such as a Youth Movement or the Boy Scouts, whose activities will appeal to him as romantic. Many activities may be useful in dealing with children of this type: e.g. sports and games of all sorts ; nature studies ; keeping pets ; collecting postage stamps, with their interesting links with strange lands ; or collecting stones, butterflies and plants. All can help to bring them into contact with real life and to guide their minds into fruitful channels.

THE DEVELOPMENT OF SPIRITUAL PERSONALITY

IN THE years before puberty, two factors appear to be of outstanding importance: the first stages in the formation of spiritual personality ; and the first stages in the formation of sexual personality. Both are essential early stages in the development of natural maturity and, with it, of the capacity for love which should be more and more enlarged with the passage of time. There is included in this process everything connected with the formation of will power and conscience, following a path which must be prepared in quite early childhood.

A change is noticeable, about the age of eight years, in the relationship of a normally developing child towards his parents. He begins to criticise them. So far, he has probably accepted his father and mother wholly without criticism, looking upon them in general as impeccable ; now he begins gradually to grasp the fact that the gods of yesterday are human beings with faults of their own. Complete confidence, based upon the notion of parental infallibility and omnipotence, fades away. " Grown-ups haven't got any sins ! " cried a little girl indignantly when she heard that her parents had been to confession. " My father can do anything ! " and " My mother knows everything ! " are typical childish sayings· These godlike attributes disappear one by one, leaving behind an often somewhat disappointing, if more realistic, picture. Bearing this in mind, sensible parents will try, in the interests of truth, to adjust at a much earlier age this exaggerated attitude towards them. But with parents of an authoritative type, this duty is usually neglected. There is then a danger that, when the image of the absolute in father and mother becomes untenable, the reaction will be excessive and may destroy the childs' faith in God the Father also.

The consequences in the field of religion may be quite devastating, as is well known, to those who understand the child mind. They can be avoided in good time if one is wise enough to lead the child to understand at an early age that, in all they do and fail to do, parents are subject to One far greater: namely to God. In this way, one may bring about a community of effort in which parents and children strive together along the path towards the perfect life, the parents acting as patterns and leaders. In such an atmosphere as this the children—even when they realise the faults of their elders—will not experience so serious and shattering a loss of confidence. One cannot be too keenly aware of the danger of being set by one's children upon a throne of idealism. We should be comrades rather than tin gods whose weaknesses will soon become only too apparent as the critical phase develops. Parents must be prepared for a natural loosening of the relationship to their children in the time of pre-puberty. Children will often show less affection ; but it should be understood that their increasing desire to stand on their own feet does not signify a lack of affection but is a necessary phenomenon in the oncoming of maturity and one whose more blatant aspects should be met with an understanding smile.

Education of the Will

In laying the foundations of the spiritual personality, the main thing is the development of will power and of conscience. In these years in particular, the adolescent takes the education of his will more and more under his control until at a later date it is wholly in his hands. The entire process is directed towards *self-determination*. The oppositional phase of puberty, with its crass and trying manifestations, must be regarded as a transitional and necessary part of this process. The adolescent is aware of the chaos within himself and makes considerable efforts to develop beyond it and thus achieve autonomy. This emancipatory process, sometimes so difficult and awkward in the forms it takes, ought not to cause indignation to adults. They would do better to remember their own youthful days and adopt an attitude of tolerant understanding.

The following anecdote was related by the mother of a boy passing through this stage : " I saw my boy coming down the street with a group of companions. When he saw me he was visibly embarrassed. They all crossed the street, stood in front of a shop window and put their heads close together. It was obvious that his budding manhood found it painful to admit that he was after all a child, by having to greet his mother in public ! "

Self-control is of great importance in the education of the will. It will be found useful to encourage children from an early period to practise little acts of self-discipline. This is much better than too much indulgence. The reasons for such small sacrifices should come from within ; they should not be prefaced with " You must ! " or " You must not ! " but should spring from the child's own decision, even if the approach has to be carefully prepared. We want the child to learn *self*-discipline—an overcoming of self, leading to freedom—not a slavish obedience. The will derives its motives from our system of values. At this point, the need of leadership for young people is especially evident, because they suffer a great deal from topsy-turvey values, not having enough experience to know what are the real interior and eternal values. They are thus a prey to all sorts of fleeting sensations and temptations, drawing them hither and thither. In most cases they find the meaning of life in what affords them pleasure. With the younger ones, the cinema and the sweet shop may be the main attractions ; but it is not long before they look further afield.

Adolescents are thus faced with this empty materialism, and with consequent unsatisfying values which may later result in anxiety neuroses about life itself. We must therefore do our utmost to include in them an appreciation of genuine values. We have a large number of factors capable of inspiring the idealism of young people: nature and animals ; music and painting ; sport and games ; singing and legends of old ; racing and hiking ; friendship and companionship—and last, but not least, religious services and genuine robust piety. Youth groups, if well led, are eminently capable of answering the need of youth for these and similar experiences with all the values they embody—even before the time of puberty in the strict sense.

Education of Conscience

This is closely connected with the education of the will. Both need interior freedom. What is commonly called " a bad conscience " is very often not an expression of true conscience ; it is no more than a consequence of external training, as we can see in the case of a dog afraid of being punished. Conscience depends upon love. One may even say that it is a function of the heart, of the power to love. Just as the latter must be developed and practised, so must conscience. It presupposes, at the least, a preparatory stage in the development of personality. Certainly such a development is not possible unless an individual realises—at least in some degree—his creative responsibility and his freedom. It is necessary, also, that the adolescent should achieve some critical objectivity so that he can form a judgment as to the truth of his inner life. In the case of a child, his inner truth is *in statu nascendi*. It is forming and striving upwards, supported by the objective truth of God, demonstrated in natural and supernatural truth. Natural truth is accessible to men through the study of the laws of nature, while faith in Revelation provides the path leading to a knowledge of the supernatural order. Our moral life rests upon both these truths.

It is the function of priests, parents, and educators to act as representatives of God and administrators of the objective order of life. Through them the child perceives and learns that law is founded upon love and directs our lives towards love. He ought to see for himself that his parents also subject themselves to the divine order. Their attitude towards the child and their own lives and conduct will determine, to a large extent, the manner in which the child will think of God ; whether it will be possible for him to have a heartfelt faith in the love of God ; and whether he will be able to place himself with all his weaknesses in the supporting hands of God, full of confidence in the venture of faith and free from the egoistic barriers and defences set up by the weak *ego*. The example and teachings of those set over him are of vital importance to the child in his development of spirit and courage. They will determine to a greater extent whether, as an adult, he will meet the problems of life freely, according to his own true inner voice and the test of objective truth, or in a slavish fashion which makes him seek security through the letter of the law and evade personal responsibility. No one can rob him of this freedom of a mature conscience ; and this alone can lead him forward, transcending self, to a true relationship to God and a genuine capacity for love. But a considerable period of development will be necessary before the needful maturity can be acquired. Puberty will carry forward the work previously done and make the boy or girl ripe for love.

Christ called men to full responsibility and freedom. He put God before us as a Father to Whom we can speak freely and with confidence as we would to an earthly father, and not as a dreaded Judge. In His own life, He demonstrated that love stands above the law and that obedience is demanded solely through love and not through fear of punishment as in the old Jewish conception. The great mass of the people of God have not yet reached the stage when they can base their actions upon the virtue of love and let their conscience be guided by the Absolute, as far as the latter is accessible to us in our present state. There is thus a sound reason for anxiety lest the more superficial types will be guided by opportunism, pursuing that which appears at the moment to be favourable or agreeable. This sort of opportunistic morality can lead only to an estrangement from moral law and conscience. It is necessary to practise honest and single-minded self-examination if one is to hear the voice of concience and obey it. How difficult it is to attain to this interior honesty emerges with peculiar clarity in the experiences of the psychiatrist.

The parents—together with the priest in his role as confessor—can be of great help to the child in the practice of *self-criticism* by doing it with him. It is excellent if the mother spends a little time with the child in the evening, going over the days' events: what was good to-day, and for what can we be grateful ? How far have we succeeded to-day in being good and in overcoming self ? And what was not good to-day ? Where have we failed to-day ? If *one* child be taken each day and, on Saturdays, all the children in preparation for communion, it will be found that in most cases it will be easy to find the time. This co-operative criticism will encourage the timid child who may be inclined to judge himself too severely ; and it will, help the child who finds it difficult to admit to anything wrong, to see his weaknesses as they are. Thus the children learn to look at themselves from outside and to adopt a right attitude towards themselves. We must, however, take care in this sort of examination that the attention of the child does not become fixed upon sin. It is a danger not to be underrated ; the child may become somewhat fascinated by the consideration of too many " sins "— more especially those connected with the sixth commandment, for in the child's mind what is dark and mysterious can exercise a fascination. Then the good and bright side of life may lose its attraction. It is a grotesque thing if a child, or its parents, keeps asking: " Is that a sin ? Shall I go to Hell ?"

THE DEVELOPMENT OF SEXUAL PERSONALITY

THE SECOND problem confronting the child growing towards maturity is the preparation of the ground with a view to a right formation of the sexual personality. It is not less important for the child's growth to full maturity than the right orientation of the spiritual and mental faculties. We must at the outset make it perfectly clear that the interest taken by children in everything to do with sex is an absolutely natural and necessary thirst for knowledge; this lies behind the early questions beginning with " why," and it is natural that there should be curiosity in this field as well as in what concerns the child himself and those around him. The problem of his own origin and that of his brothers and sisters has very likely already intrigued him. Three to four years is the usual period when such interest is consciously present to the child's mind.   The arrival of younger brother or sister—often far from welcome—disturbs his little world and stimulates questions. Now is the time for giving honest answers !

If a child does not to all appearances take any interest in these things and continues this lack of curiosity up to school age, then we may assume that some inhibition, generally unconscious, is checking the natural development of curiosity. The inhibition may be due to inadequate replies to question that were asked, to the feeling that they were not welcome, or possibly because of experiences in the parents' bedroom, or, as is frequently the case, to a home atmosphere which tends to crush curiosity along such lines. We have dealt in some detail with the problem of sex enlightenment, the dangers of stork stories etc., and the right method of approach, in the volume entitled *Difficulties in Sex Education*.

In the years of pre-puberty, the main thing is the part played by sex in the life of the child himself. Amongst children who have not been rightly initiated in these matters by parents or others, there is always a serious danger that information as to fatherhood and motherhood may be sought unknown to the parents in most un-savoury quarters. We are all aware of the disgusting fashion in which most children learn about sex. They do not form even the remotest conception of human *love*, the most significant factor of all. At best, the marriage union is put before them on the same level as the mating of animals on a farm. In this age of awakening curiosity careful supervision and guidance by parents is vitally important. This supervision must not, however, take the form of keeping the children in a glass house; this can only increase curiosity and the pressure of growing instincts. The disastrous consequences of such treatment are well known ; the child hitherto so sheltered goes out into the world with a new freedom, but with no idea of how to protect himself and meet the test of real life.

The Negative Phase

Many children pass through a phase of peculiar difficulty just before puberty. The patience of parents or others in charge is liable to be strained to breaking point. This we may call the negative phase. The children are bent on achieving a degree of independence in excess of the actual development of their bodily, mental, and spiritual powers. They make difficulties about their lessons ; they are restless under discipline ; and they often retire into an attitude of sheer stubbornness. In a good many cases we observe rapid changes from an unusual demonstrative tenderness to the most extreme attitude of secretiveness and distrust. Behind all this is anxiety as to the unknown which awaits the child in the future and is dimly realised by him. This unknown is felt to be full of demands, threatening and, in a vague way, even frightening, like some dream figure knocking at the door. This state of anxiety gives rise to all sorts of modes of escape: rebelliousness, untruth-fulness, separation, and minor thefts. The most striking mani-festations of this negative mood are the attacks of *depression* which may occur from time to time.

A student told me: " I was eleven years old. One day I was lying in bed half-asleep when suddenly I was overwhelmed by a nameless fear which seemed to come from a dark corner of the room ; I thought I had to die, and felt I was being strangled. Cold sweat broke out and my heart beat until I felt it would burst. For several hours I lay in the grip of this terror. For weeks afterwards, when I went to bed I was terrified to think this experience might return." In other words, fear of fear. The consequence was a state of depression lasting for months ; and exercising a decisive influence in checking the boy's progress towards maturity. Ten years later, when he began to study for his career and was faced with important decisions, the depression returned with renewed vigour. Under psychoanalytical treatment he recognised that, in respect of his sexual development, he had failed to mature, and had remained fixed at the pre-puberal stage. In the process of re-education follow-ing upon his analysis, he had to go back and pick up the lost threads. His fear of death was felt by him as a threat to his existence—but not in a bodily sense ; nor was it fear of a judgment after death. What was threatened was the existence of his *ego*. The uprising of a new and not yet understanable force was unconsciously felt in the depths of the soul to constitute a peril to the rule of reason over the personality.

The sexual urges follow their own laws and are capable of over-throwing the laws that rule in the conscious mind. Hence they were regarded by the ancient world and by Judaism as demonic powers. They form the *id* of the psychoanalytical school—this *id* having an autonomous existence which makes it independent of the higher self of the soul.

If we bear in mind how long the definition of the soul as reason and free will was generally accepted, we cannot be surprised that the unconscious was frequently looked upon as alien and threatening and that the sexual—which so often causes us to do what we had no real intention of doing—bore the character of the demoniacal and evil down to the late Middle Ages. Even to-day we have to reckon with this dark view of sex.

Many people are afraid of the unknown depths in their own souls, and to escape from this threat they make themselves believe that it is first and foremost a question of the rule of the conscious *ego*, of reason and will. They have a special dread of the animal-sexual urge glimpsed during puberty and later still more developed. It is in fact often stronger then the *ego*, more especially during the chaotic period of puberty.

Their concern for personal purity causes many young people to suffer from a state of inhibition, a cramping of the personality which is difficult to overcome. There may be no conscious thought of sex. The feeling that the *ego* is threatened and, with it, the idealised picture of this *ego* in their own eyes and those of the world, is often enough to bring about the suppression of the *id*, with its deep urges, and by way of compensation, the overemphasis of the rational.

The child is in very special need of our encouragement and guidance in the face of all these difficulties, if his confidence in himself and in life is to be consolidated. Otherwise, there is a real danger that he may fail to develop normally and remain fixed in the inhibited state just described.

DELAYED PUBERTY

IN NORMAL cases, the beginning of puberty signifies the overcoming of the negative phase. It ends when the various types of escapism have been found to lead nowhere, and the effort to achieve a mature life strenghtens. With girls this can take place quite suddenly with the first menstruation. But if this is not the case, if the tendency to withdraw from the world remains dominant, then we have to deal with pathological elements. Those are usually caused by too little love, by a lack of help, or by wrong sex education. Let us consider three cases:

A case of bed-wetting. Robert was eleven years old and still frequently wet his bed. Attempts to cure this habit, by means of either kindness or severity, failed. His mother was a widow and, as a teacher, she was particularly anxious to see her boy do well ; but owing to her own unsatisfactory childhood experiences and her too short married life she became so egocentric that her little boy suffered from inadequate love in the home. Further, he had a little sister three years younger, who was continually held up as an example by the mother. It is a striking fact that his bad habit was always worse when his mother was nervous, impatient, over-worked, severe, or unloving, and that he improved when she gave him more attention and made some effort to understand him.

The bed-wetting of this boy—who was described as difficult also in other ways—can be looked upon as a demand to be treated as a small child: he felt that he was not getting enough attention, he yearned for more love from the mother and more security. He wanted to stay a child, with a child's claim to receive love, and all his reactions showed a powerful mother-fixation. This held him back from making progress towards independence and maturity. The relationship between mother and son was made more difficult by his behaviour. The more difficult he was, the more disappointed she became, especially as she had set her hopes high, and the more she tended to be severe with him. The vicious circle is obvious. Despite good abilities and lively reactions Robert remained backward and was by far the meanest boy in his class.

The mother finally took advice from psychotherapists and the underlying reasons for her boy's difficulties were made clear. She made earnest efforts, not always with success, to better her attitude. In time she did succeed, and the boy not only overcame his bed wetting, but strove energetically to behave better towards his mother and began to exhibit signs that he was actually entering into the world of puberty at last.

Hardly worth-while trying. Delays in puberty can arise by reason of the position of a child in the family : this is most often witnessed with the youngest, if the attitude of the elder children is not such as to protect him against discouragement. The life-pattern of the elder brothers and sisters is apt to be overwhelming ; they seem so far above and beyond that the youngest is utterly damped. If they can never be caught up with, the struggle appears hardly worth while. What is the use of growing up and becoming mature ? If, on top of this, we find a wrong type of education and environmental influence, the underdevelopment of the youngest can assume the most glaring forms.

Hildegard, aged 14, was the youngest ; her three sisters were already students on a level which the young one could never aspire to reach. Moreover, her gifts were of a less intellectual type ; she liked housework and home life, the garden and the stable. The father was strict and authoritarian. He was possibly disappointed in the relatively poor school record of the girl and he made the mistake of adopting a severe attitude towards her failures ; she felt this deeply and became even more uncertain and more convinced of her inferiority. The little girl was conspicuously childish and undeveloped, physically as well as mentally. Her appearance was that of a child of eight and she was smaller than the other girls in her class.

Hildegard represented a type not seldom found in schools : strikingly childish and extremely uncertain of herself, the latter point emerging sharply in her written work where all her mistakes stood out in black and white. The teacher explained that she was much better in oral work. It is a point of some interest that when the written work is much better than the oral, or vice versa, and when there is a discrepancy between age and stage of development, we should not fail to pay special attention to the child. A signal has been given that encouragement is urgently needed, plenty of praise, and little tasks calculated to inspire confidence ; we should notice what is good, and create a calm, friendly, encouraging, and sheltering atmosphere. These are some of the little things that a good teacher will know to be needful in such a case.

Married, yet she still believes in the stork. Until the age of thirteen, Marga slept with her parents. Nevertheless, the experiences which the child must have had left no trace on her memory ; or, to be more correct, they were thrust down in the mind, because they were painful to her. As we might expect from the above, the atmosphere in the home was such that all questions dealing with sex were immediately frozen, and absolutely nothing took place to introduce the girl to realities. Her mother scarcely bothered with the child at all ; she got no help of any kind. The girl had a feeling of physical distaste for her mother, but she was attracted to her father. This state of affairs can be connected readily with the matter of the sleeping arrangements and the experiences thrust down into the subconscious.

This wholly unprepared child experienced her first menstruation at the age of seventeen. Even then, she did not feel able to ask any questions of a sexual nature. At twenty, on the advice of her mother, she married a man she did not love, while she was still without even a remote idea of what marriage meant. It was only after she had given birth to a baby that she knew where babies came from ! At the age of fifty, mother of grown-up children, she was, essentially, an immature girl : insecure in every way, full of feeling of interiority, terrified of responsibility and decision. She had absolutely no sound relationship to the bodily and organic side of life, and her religious development was, of necessity, frustrated.

To achieve true maturity, such a case has to overtake the developments that, properly speaking, should have taken place during puberty. But we can imagine the difficulty of facing the problems of puberty during the so-called " change of life."

The lesson to be drawn is that, when we meet with sexually backward children this must be regarded as a danger signal. Such cases are in urgent need of help; we have to assist them to establish a harmonious relationship to their bodies and sex nature, thus promoting their normal progress towards maturity, physical, mental, and spiritual.

It is a well-established fact, based on experience, that the bodily foundation must be set in order first, and upon this the mental and spiritual can be built up in organic fashion. If the parents prove unequal to giving the children this organic education, one of the most valuable gifts that can be bestowed upon one starting in life, then somebody else must step in to fill the gap ; teacher, priest, youth-leader, doctor, or other understanding guide.

Part II

CHILD INTO MAN

In the period which precedes puberty the basic attitude of the child is one of extraversion ; his face is turned towards the outer world. This is conditioned by the fact that he has to come to terms with the world and to find his way about in all that surrounds him. In the early days of puberty, however, we note a tendency towards introversion, a direction of attention inwards. He notices his own individuality, the self rooted in his essential inner being. He is aware of the division within himself and of how he now stands apart wanting to draw away from the hitherto accepted world of the grown-ups. This is the outward aspect of his new development. Yet, at the same time, he feels an inward conflict : the child still within him carries on a struggle against the awakening feeling : " I am no longer a child." His attention is drawn towards his inner life and he seeks to understand the new forces and feelings beginning to stir within him.

GROWING OUT OF CHILDHOOD

The stage when a child feels the urge to break away from adults and try out his own wings is very trying for the parent or educator. What this development really signifies is, more than anything else, a detachment on the child's part from a portion of his own life which he now feels he has outgrown: namely, the world of childish life. Within its borders it was always the adults who managed things and made all the decisions. They carried all the responsibility. To bring about the needful development of conscience and the growth of freedom and responsibility, the child must obey the inward urge towards a more individual life.

It is most important that parents and others in charge of children should realise clearly that this revolution in the child's attitude is necessary, and they must exercise patience and understanding even when this is not easy. If we find a child lacking in this urge to break away, then we can be sure something is wrong ; he is not developing normally. Perhaps there is a desire to escape the responsibilities of growing up, a lack of self-confidence which makes the child prefer to leave decisions and responsibility in adult hands. Or, on the other hand, the parents may be to blame, because they are not willing to grant the child the necessary freedom ; perhaps their attitude is more that of the authoritative master than that of the responsible steward.

The Oppositional Phase of Puberty

The adolescent strives to manage his own life, to decide for himself what he should do and not do. This is a healthy development in which he seeks to become an individual, to be mature, responsible and manly. He will look upon the commands and rules of adults as unjustified interferences with his newly found liberties and capacities, and for this reason he will develop an oppositional state of mind.

But since he is as yet no more than a *learner* and is not fully able to manage his life, his attempt to achieve autonomy will certainly lead to differences with adults. It is remarkable how many parents fail to understand the revolution that goes on in the adolescent mind, although they have all been through it themselves.

The type of opposition is likely to alter with the age and its forms. For example, the attitude of German youth after the first World War differed markedly from the present-day attitude. The keynote in the earlier period was rebellion against the forms of bourgeois life, with a seeking of new forms based upon a return to nature—although the latter were as strict in their own way as those of the older generation. It was then felt amongst young people that the face-saving attitude of their elders was not truthful and genuine, so that youth preferred the path of " inner truthfulness."

It is quite possible to believe that the youth of to-day looks upon " making up " as a form of opposition, marking off their separation from the formlessness of their parents ; or that their crass realism is a reaction against the romantic idealism of the earlier youth movements. All this does not make the young people of to-day any worse. Leonhard Seiff said of those who were filled with the spirit of opposition: " The obstinate defiant type never knows what he wants until he finds out what the *other* wants—then he takes the opposite side."

Therefore, it is wise to be quite clear in our minds that an immense amount of patience and love may be called for in our dealings with the restless fermentation of the new wine of youth. Left in peace, it will become clear and grow more mature. The educator will do well to hold back, to wait, to say little and overlook much. The right word at the right time may do no harm, but nothing should be done to make the process of self-realisation more difficult for the adolescent by too obvious guidance or, worse still, by a too active interference or an authoritarian attitude. The personal life of the adolescent, even in this stage of immaturity, must be accepted for what it is and be respected ; this will make things much easier for him in his struggle to achieve recognition as a mature individual. For he who has achieved self-realisation will no longer strive to assert himself:

and he must not forget that if the youthful urge towards autonomy is suppressed there is a danger that the adolescent will fail to develop beyond the mental and moral stage of puberty.

Such an inhibition yields, later on, adults who either remain in a state of childish dependence—presenting sometimes a touching picture of childlike affection—or become confirmed rebels, men who have taken the first step by opposing authority, but have never developed a positive individual attitude. We again come into contact with the obstinate and defiant type mentioned above. If the child is able to exercise his development of will in defiance and opposition, if he is given a fair opportunity to make use of his will in some rational way instead of encouraging at every turn a blank " No !", then, not only will the manifestations of rebellion be milder, but this stage will in the end be more easily overcome. If, on the other hand, the stubborn will is " broken," then the individual will remain all his life fixed in this stage. Thus parents will do well to allow their children plenty of freedom. After all, we know that they must live their own lives: no one can do this for them. At the same time, we can help young people by enabling them to obtain a better understanding of themselves. They often suffer quite severely through inner conflicts at this stage of development, and cannot by themselves fathom their own minds.

The adolescent does not understand his own inner nature, while at the same time he feels that adults cannot understand him. This is a natural phenomenon of this stage of growth. When the hormones from the sex glands pass into the blood and begin to do their work, the whole personality of the boy or girl becomes filled with new urges, and there is a vigorous growing and budding as the system prepares itself for manhood or womanhood. But the young person does not know how to bring the newly awakened powers under control and establish harmony.

The result is the well known awkwardness, the " coltishness " of young people at this age. They stumble over their feet, get their arms and legs all entangled, do not know how to behave properly, and are cross with themselves on this account. But they really cannot help it,; so they get irritable with others and become noisy and aggressive. We all know the boy who demonstrates his manhood by trampling about the house like a young elephant. If the other people in the house object, he will probably react by whistling as well as trampling about !

Boys and girls are often seriously unhappy during this period. We should explain to them, patiently, just *why* they are so oppositional, defiant, and annoying. But if we bring severe pressure to bear upon them in the home they will get more and more impossible elsewhere. No tree or wall, no windows or gardens, no human beings or animals in the whole neighbourhood will be safe from their expanding energies. But if the home atmosphere is one of greater understanding and more freedom, all these reactions can be brought within more reasonable bounds.

The feeling of not being understood, the view that, childhood being over, there is no path towards adult life open to them, causes many young people to experience sensations of infinite loneliness and abandonment. Inwardly, they cry out for someone to help them, but they seek to present an outward appearance of being unapproachable. They put on airs of superiority, make an impression of arrogance, and exhibit a degree of self-complacency that is utterly opposed to their inward insecurity and helplessness.

Life in the Community

The attitude of opposition, the breaking away from parental control, is a stage towards the formation of a new tie. It is necessary that youth should fly out of the nest, that boys and girls should look further afield than the family and seek to establish, of their own free choice, ties of a more mature kind. Such a new connection is only possible if the boy or girl takes it up of their own free will and co-operates responsibly in its formation. The period of passive absorption in the family circle thus comes to an end, as maturity draws near.

The new connection and companionship is usually different from what the individual has known through childhood. It is self-chosen in accordance with the spirit of independence now developing. While it is necessary that the adolescent, in the first place, should separate himself from the old ties and become free to form new associations, it is possible for the new ties to be formed by the former family connections. Now the boy becomes an active co-operating member. Sometimes the processes of separation and re-association follow one another so rapidly that, seen from outside, they are barely noticeable. In most cases the new connection is formed with a new set of people ; this is more especially the case if the family relationships are difficult or disturbed.

It will often be a great help to the young if they are able to choose between already existing youth groups or associations of friends. The right sort of youth leader can serve as a pattern of young manhood and awaken all that is idealistic in youth. A boy will hasten to follow such a leader and his progress towards a mature participation in the outer world will be correspondingly quickened. The boy will now feel that he is understood. He knows, or at least dimly realises, that the others in his circle are struggling with similar difficulties and problems and thus he looses his former isolation and separatist attitude. Again he has now found a WE, and the idealism with which he recognises this new companionship and community is highly characteristic of puberty.

The most favourable conditions are indicated when *youth is led by youth*. Then the great gulf which exists between young people and fully developed adults is bridged. The pattern set before the adolescent seems nearer and more attainable, and hence more encouraging. However, it is of course advantageous if a mature personality—a priest, say—occupies a higher position as spiritual director ; this will be especially useful in the training of leaders of groups. But such a higher authority will do well to remain in the background as adviser.

If the movement away from self towards the outer world does not develop spontaneously through instinctive urges, it becomes necessary to assist the adolescent. But we should be on our guard against obvious guidance, lest oppositional forces resisting adult control come into play. During this phase the adolescent is very sensitive as to any steps tending to place him amongst the younger set. True authority need not suffer through this caution.

Any linking up with a group involves certain *demands* upon the individual, and for this reason many young people are afraid of these ties. They do not feel equal to the claims that may be made. They feel insecure and tend to take up an attitude of indecision. They have probably already taken the step of protesting against the early ties ; but the protest is not so much against family and authority as against the lack of freedom and self-determination attached to the state of childhood. They have failed to use their increased freedom to forge new links. They lack confidence in their own value which they know will have to be proved in the new community.

It is from the ranks of these types that the figure of the stubborn self-centred individualist emerges: the man who is never prepared to place his whole self at the service of others ; the egoist who is always ready to *receive* love, but cannot find the courage to risk active love and sacrifice. This type cannot become a " partner " in any real sense, for his heart is never turned outwards towards another ; he cannot enter into the needs or limitations of others. He may be capable of a vague generalised philanthropy, but not of a genuine personal love directed towards helping and saving another. Such a one suffers ultimately, perhaps secretly, through his lack of real contacts and warm human relationships, and through the loneliness that ensues.

Yet it is not impossible for him, if he realises that his inward attitude is wrong, to pick up the broken threads of his life at a later age and strive to recover something of what was missed. This will require a courageous effort to go outside himself, the same effort that was previously lacking. But he must learn *to venture*. If the anxieties and inhibitions, together with the lack of self-confidence and general feeling of insecurity, are too formidable, the individual will hardly be able, without expert psychotherapeutic guidance, to take the forward path towards a vital contact with life.

MENTAL AND SPIRITUAL EDUCATION

IN THE case of all education, the main thing is that somebody—or better, something—is there to attract the individual to be educated. Even in his role as model, the educator should lead the pupil only indirectly. It is best that he should lead the youth to see the goal aimed at, and help him to attain to it himself. That is organic education: otherwise we have mere organisation—or even, what is worse, mechanical training.

For all men, a goal is that which appears good and worthy of pursuit ; beautiful, valuable, true, and lasting. A goal must promise happiness, satisfaction, and even blessedness. A goal acts as a call, a summons. The urge to erotic love is the answer to the call of instinct. The moral force of the human being evaluates the various goals and selects the most worthy.

Discipline is, accordingly, the employment of the basic urges in harmony with the moral order of values. To be educated is to choose the most valuable goal. With the undisciplined character the instinctive urges are directed, not towards the highest in accordance with the moral order, but towards the nearest goal promising an *easy* satisfaction—even if this be devoid of value. Such a type draws away from the claims of his spiritual and moral nature, urging him to choose the best.

The higher development of humanity leads from the lower level of the vegetative (preservation of life) and the animal (preservation of the species) through the field of emotional formation to the moral and spiritual. At the time of puberty, the newly awakened activity of the sexual glands conditions the ripening of the animal-sexual nature. We deal with this aspect in detail later. First we turn to the moral and spiritual aspect. Maturity is here reached by way of the erotic urge.

The Emotional Stage

The emotional corresponds with the lowest of the three steps in spiritual development as described by Kierkegaard. He begins with the aesthetic and holds that the spiritual awakening of the majority of people does not get beyond this. The next stage is the ethical, concerned with good and evil, with the fulfilment of life in an ordered system of values. This is reached by an appreciably smaller number of individuals. The third and highest stage, the religious, the vital contact with the process of salvation, is attained by only a very few.

It is the task of mental and spiritual puberty to pursue this process of development. It will go on right into the years of mature manhood and womanhood—if the subject is sufficiently differentiated to be *able* to develop so far. We can say indeed that this process never ends ; stagnation implies regression.

During the early period of puberty, the regulative forces are lacking, both in the instinctive life itself and in the inner life of the emotions, in as far as these forces are influenced by the will. For the latter is determined by the hierarchy of values. The young man or woman must be educated in these values if the development of his erotic life is to follow the right path.

The formation of the emotional world is a task falling to the adolescent in the later years of puberty. It is at this period that we find the exaggeration and instability of emotional life so typical of puberty. We all know the " crushes " and emotional excitements of the adolescent school-girl, and the early manifestations of " falling in love." The face of the adolescent blushes with embarrassment when such things are mentioned, as if he had been caught on some forbidden ground, for this is the time for every sort of unbalanced and chaotic emotionalism.

The world of feeling must be explored and purified. The young are highly sensitive, but are not able to achieve the needful mastery over feeling. Hence the irrational feelings of repulsion, the preoccupied modes, the rapid changes from exaltation to deep depression, and the inability to control likes and dislikes. The later years of puberty are often characterised by sentimentality. This is the time of meaningless verses, songs dripping with sentiment and—when this is possible—musical compositions filled with yearning. It is the time, too, when the moon is cultivated as a friend and confidant, and is called upon to receive sighs of inexpressible emotion. She looks down upon the earth with a knowing smile ; she is well acquainted with the sufferings of young hearts !

Gradually, however, as the nervous system becomes more stable, the chaotic emotional life clarifies itself and the impressions of the adolescent grow deeper, more inward, and nearer to reality. The spiritual forces strengthen and become able to donimate the feelings instead of being dominated by them. Thus it is quite normal if young people are overtaken by storms of an emotional nature ; it is a stage in self-realisation. They must not be afraid of venturing and, within the bounds of moral order, must accept the stormy emotions of youth. As they become spiritually mature, the emotions will take their place in the system of values which controls the evolution towards mature sexuality. Instead of being the centre of life, the emotional will become a species of accompaniment, colouring and enriching life. The more experience is assimilated the more depth and reality it has, the more genuine and free from exaggeration and strain will be the emotional life.

But many people never attain to this state of true maturity. They remain unstable, subject to their moods and to the sway of feeling. They measure their own value and that of others solely according to the aesthetic standards which dominate their life pattern.

This applies equally to the *religious* side of life. The elevation of the heart towards God—the *sursum corda*—is purely emotional. The trappings of religion are esteemed at the expense of its inner reality. Thus we get great enthusiams for oratories, religious music, and pomp and ceremonial, without which a religious service must seem empty and dead. The reality and vitality of religion is measured by these types, in terms of the emotions it arouses, and many of them suffer despair if they feel their emotions are not satisfied. This may cause much suffering in periods of spiritual dryness. Then it becomes only too clear that the religious side of personality is not adequately spiritualised and is poor in itself ; and complaints are heard about the dryness of the services by which God is worshipped. We are told that they cannot pray and that God is not alive in their hearts.

Similar experiences befall these types in the field of *human* love. Happiness is measured by the extent of subjective emotional life. The emotion of love is the starting point of the relationship ; but it does not prove an adequate foundation for a lasting union in real life. The life of the spirit, with the dynamic of good-will, is an essential element in this foundation ; without it, the union of two human beings cannot be shaped in a truly vital manner. When feeling alone is dominant, we have a shell without a kernel, pretty to look at, perhaps, but without substance. Times of crisis bring this out forcibly. For feeling does not obey orders and it cannot be pledged. But we can pledge love until death—a love that never ceases its dynamic action on behalf of the partner and the creation of a true common life.

The psychology of the unconscious teaches us that those whose experience is lacking in depth and intensity try to compensate for this deficiency by an exaggerated development of the emotional and subjective elements. They have a vague feeling that they owe a debt to themselves—and to their partners also in many cases. Such a state is likely to lead to an inhibition of emotion, and to hysterical subjective moods, in place of real depth of feeling.

Feelings can so easily be deceptive. Consider the case of conscience. How often the feeling of a quiet or of a guilty conscience completely fails to express the reality ; the individual often succeeds in lulling his conscience and silencing its voice ; while, in many neurotic cases, the true voice is diverted to a concern for the meticulous performance of a host of external actions—such performance yielding a substitute satisfaction. In the case of neurotic subjects, feelings of guilt, inferiority, and lack of confidence can deceive the subject to an extraordinary degree. Knowledge springing from the vital centre of being can assign its proper place to feeling, and allot the leadership to the dynamic spiritual forces coming from the heart.

The neurotic is to be looked upon, not as a man who has lost his freedom of action by reason of inhibitions and ties on the subconscious level, but as one who has never *really* gained this freedom. His treatment should thus consist, not in liberating him from psychic suffering, but in helping him to attain to self-discovery.

Idealism

We have already pointed out how necessary it is to bring the adolescent into contact with life-aims adapted to his disposition, and have mentioned the suitability of youth groups in this respect. The exploration of the countryside reveals a quite new world to many young people, filling their hearts with joy. New scenes, the romantic aspects of nature, contact with animals in their native haunts : all help to feed the natural love of adventure and the longing for some distant paradise so charactertistic of the young mind. Songs, music, myths and legends of old, give wings to the imagination of youth and aid the development of the emotional life. Sport and games of all sorts provide the best openings for the natural urge towards activity and expansion.

The adolescent is inwardly thankful for every genuine experience of new values such as he may receive, for example, through comradeship which inculcates mutual help and regard for others, youthful chivalry, and sound religious life. Nowadays, when so much confusion has been caused by two great wars, the mass of young folk are sadly lacking in appreciation of real values, and their elders and educators must exercise the utmost care in directing the attention of adolescents towards aims and purposes in harmony with their inmost life-urge.

The child of to-day from his earliest days is exposed to superficial influences such as the cinema, radio, trashy magazines and children's papers, all calculated to weaken his deeper feelings. The danger is that, in this way, he will lose the delicacy of touch and emotional responsiveness requisite for appreciating the finer things of life. Absorption in the regular and the blatant, the sensational and the pretentious, is always so much easier. It takes a great deal of patience and good-will to re-educate such a modern child to an appreciation of the best.

He whose senses are wide-awake and receptive to fine perceptions and moods, and who knows how to look and listen, finds beauty, created by God, everywhere ; and his heart is filled with gratitude. Such a man can never become wholly discontented or filled with despair. His heart has been opened wide to appreciate true moral values and grasp the reality of faith. Take care, however, especially at first, not to approach young people in the role of a preacher ! During these years, the path to religion passes usually through the aesthetic values and, after that, through the ethical. Thus the young spirit ripens and is ready to experience a living relationship to God.

It is by means of the right example that the adolescent is set upon the path of moral and spiritual self-education, the goal of true educa- tion. He will accept guidance from someone in whom he sees a convincing pattern of behaviour, and he will become enthusiastic about higher aims. For the sake of forming himself, he will develop fanatical faith in principles, and will accept maxims as guides, if he feels they will help him along the road to self-perfection. This last motive, the quest for self-betterment, provides motives which are capable of feeding the moral and religious life for a lengthy period. Such guides—like good intentions—are no more than aids of use during a period of transition for those not yet fully mature. They come to the adolescent from outside ; he takes them up eagerly and allows himself to be influenced. This does not prove that they have become part of his inner life, but only that they are found accept- able to the mind of the adolescent. Gradually, however, with the aid of such transitional measures, the inner heart-felt development can come about, in which duty gives way to inclination: " Thou shalt!" is replaced by, " I will ! "

Many well-meaning adults come to grief in their treatment of the young on this matter of " duty " or " inclination." If the personal life-urge in the world of instinct—and of sex instinct especially—is suppressed, as being evil or dangerous, the higher spiritual energies cannot fail to suffer. In consequence, all that can be placed under the heading of " heart " or " love " will remain underdeveloped, or even be totally destroyed. If the development of the spiritual energies is to go forward, it is essential that the underlying urges of the vegetative-animal level should not be suppressed.

The best guiding principles, however much they may appeal to the intellect, will prove one day to be vain and empty if they are not vitalised by the heart itself. Unless they are so vitalised they will cease to be a help and become mere ballast; this can happen in the later days of puberty. Then one is too old to be able to find satisfaction and a meaning in life from principles and maxims. If, in the meantime, the individual has not found a life-conception of his own, a pattern of meaningful life that he can inwardly accept, he will one day find that heart and hands are empty. He will have no adequate instrument to shape his life. The adolescent who has sought to mould his existence, in a spiritual sense, upon some idealistic life-outlook imposed upon him from outside, and has not succeeded in making this truly a part of himself, will find that the ideals he looked up to will gradually lose their power and fade away. As the years pass by, he will discover that they are not fed with the nourishing sap of real life. He may seek, with the utmost determination, to hold fast to a sense of duty sustained by his reason, but the time will come when he is overtaken by dull resignation, and the real core of his life will wither.

In the most favourable type of case, the individual perceives that he is on the wrong track, his conscience is aroused, and he endeavours to reform his life. If the suppressed energies are still strong enough, and the will to save his soul and find true self-expression is not too weak and blunted, his inner energies may break through and force a path leading upwards. We may then have a spiritual crisis and the suppressed forces may reveal themselves in manifestations of mental or physical illness: thus it is not uncommon to find, during middle age, such symptoms as strong states of anxiety, depressions, or obsessional illnesses. In the physical field, we meet with all sorts of neuroses and illnesses with a psychic derivation: disturbances of the heart, stomach, glandular system, insomnia, headaches, alarming attacks of cramp, and other conditions. Such crisis symptoms must be taken as signals of alarm, as cries sent up by the innermost self indicating the need for self-recollection and for a new orientation of life. Fortunate is the man who knows that he should consult a psychotherapist at this stage, who will enable him to dig up the recesses of the subconscious and remove the factors blocking up the approaches to heart and conscience. If this step is not taken, the subject is likely to sink into a more or less mummified condition of resignation, perhaps dignified by some other name—such as modesty or shyness.

In normal cases, maturity of mind and character brings about a decisive development during the third decade, especially in a man. He now takes himself in hand thoroughly, unless his evolution has been in some way hindered: he overcomes the indecision and tentative attitude of adolescence, and with self-discipline, firm action, clarity of purpose, and endurance, he strides forward into real manhood.

With a woman it is different. In the first decades she matures more rapidly, largely as a result of her closer affinity to the organic life of nature. The man is more bound up with the mental and spiritual side of life. The development to full womanhood depends to a lesser degree upon the relatively slow development of the mental and spiritual side. For the same reason, the crisis of maturity makes less impression in an outward sense ; it has more the character of a natural process, and as the woman remains nearer to childhood than the man, the transition to maturity is easier. It is fairly common to find that a full sense of responsibility and personal decision does not develop until the " change of life " ; before that time she tends to lean on the man.

From Idealism to Love

All the ideals which can fire the imagination of youth and which seem to the adolescent worthy of effort, serve as aids in overcoming his interior division. The urge driving the adolescent forward may acquire quite an alarming character when the sexual nature awakens, for now he becomes aware of an inner force having its own laws, of an alien power threatening the supremacy of the mental and moral nature, while at the same time the life-urge has not found its true goal.

Gebsattel, in his study of parents as guides during adolescence, deals with the transformation of early sexual impulse into imaginative activity. The actual goal of instinct is replaced by imaginary constructions, thus making it possible for the instinct that secretly feeds these fantasies to find a temporary mode of fulfilment and satisfaction, pending the completion of maturity. The deep need of the young to devote themselves and seek completion—a need as yet unaware of its ultimate sexual purpose—turns to other fields of expression. This explains the enthusiasm of adolescents for nature and art and their obvious erotic tendencies.

Spiritual and physical progress towards maturity do not run parallel ; the development of sexual life proceeds along two tracks. The boy, especially, remains on the undeveloped level of puberty, in a mental and spiritual sense, long after his physical nature has attained to a full development of sexual functions. The healthily

developed boy, who has not suffered any corruption, has as yet no
idea of the purpose of this function in a human and spiritual sense.

Gradually the two tracks come together. If the boy does not lose
his purity through seduction or premature sex experiences, and if
he has retained his capacity for genuine love, the bodily and spiritual
forces will merge in creating a loving union with one of the opposite
sex ; but this does not usually take place save after some years and
probably after various mistakes.

In the first place, the erotic *excludes* the sexual. If the latter
becomes active in the period of mid-maturity—around the ages of
17 and 18—this is a kind of desecration. It is true that the sexual
often invades the life of the adolescent, perhaps through curiosity or
lack of good guidance or of the idealistic element in personality ;
but it is spiritually empty and is a cause of serious damage to the
capacity for genuine love. For the formation of personality and the
discovery of self are then far from complete, and both are essential
for any genuine love between man and woman.

The premature uniting of the two tracks—the spiritual aspect of
love-life and the physical—is dangerous ; the combined force
resulting from the union may now be directed towards an individual
of the opposite sex, and the awakening instinct will grow more
urgent in its desire for physical expression, Yet the life of instinct,
despite physical development, is not yet mature. It needs to be
spiritualised and further developed before it is ready for mature
love. Young people who do not understand this are in danger of
entering into some superficial and unreal sexual contact. The
idealistic side of the sexual nature may be awakened, the subject
may love all that is good and beautiful in the partner and the sexual
side may lend energy and desire ; yet, all the while, there is no real
heart-felt urge, nothing actually transcending the animal level
and the corresponding emotions on the ideal side.

The heart is not yet ready for the love that *gives* and serves, for
the venture that involves devotion and responsibility for the welfare
of the other. Accordingly, the sexual expression of instinct does not,
at this stage, yield genuine satisfaction. It is more likely that
disappointment will result ; for the heart will remain unsatisfied
and empty. Physical union is not to be looked upon as complete in
itself, because it finds its true meaning and fulfilment only as the
physical manifestation of a love springing from the heart.

The help of an older guide or leader is very valuable at this stage,
if he understands how to enlist the young mind and heart in the
effort to raise life to a worthy level. He can appeal to the ethical
personality and make it clear that the young man should prepare
himself further for the difficult career of marriage and parenthood ;

that love must first be learned if it is to yield its best fruits, whereas a premature sexual union will prevent the ripening of these fruits. At this stage *protection* is better than *possession*.

Nor should we overlook the high educational and formative value of the heroic element, often so strong with the young, prompting them to reject the easier and choose the more difficult of two paths, as the more manly course.

Rilke once said that if one sees two possibilities, one easy and the other difficult, then, from the standpoint of personal development, the latter should be chosen just because it is the more difficult. It is clear that a certain degree of personal and social stability is desirable as a preliminary to full self-realisation. Only then, as a complete man, can he make his choice of a partner.

With adolescents it is a fact of experience that educational achievement goes down by as much as 75 per cent when a boy or girl is too much occupied with thoughts of sex. The flirtations and " petting " common in adolescence tend to check mental development and growth towards general maturity. Many writers on adolescence and its problems have pointed out a connection between early marriage and unsatisfactory cultural development. Sexual polarity and erotic tension are fruitful courses of mental inspiration: thus it is not good if a young man or woman, through premature physical expression, loses the impetus conveyed by these sources. At a later date, both the sexual and erotic will be ripe for fulfilment.

Such wisdom and restraint does not by any means imply ostracism from the other sex, or any suppression of sexual nature. Adolescents of both sexes should certainly meet and, within proper limits, take measure of each other, for, after all, the choice of a partner presupposes some knowledge of the opposite sex. And we must remember that to be a young Christian does not mean to be a boy or girl without normal sex feelings.

If a youth leader who lacks the needful insight tries to hinder young people from meeting those of the opposite sex, he runs a risk of losing his hold over them ; in any case, he is doing something to hold them back in their growth towards maturity. It is most unwise to wax indignant with adolescents when they fall in love. The decline of our civilisation is not due to an excess of instinct, but to a negative element that accompanies it—egocentricity.

The problem of the fear of love has been dealt with in our book, *Difficulties in Married Life*. But we may here mention a particular case which bears upon the present argument. A young woman student stated that she feared she could not remain faithful and loyal, should she ever marry. She had noticed that she was very changeable, now caring for one man, now for another, but never committing herself. In fact she did not *want* love, for she felt she was too young and immature for any lasting tie. Later, however, she admitted that there was a deeper reason: she was afraid of the awakening of her sexual nature through love.

If a young man accepts the principle that he will not make the venture of love until he sees the way to a final lasting union, a danger can arise: he may be too late in learning *how* to venture and to love. Thus he may contract a marriage which, through lack of emotional experience, is not based upon the right foundation or upon a right choice of partner. When this is realised, it is too late ; the facts cannot be altered. What can be altered is solely his own attitude. But when the foundation is not truly laid, it will be difficult to acquire the virtue of love. Loving does not mean that the last surrender must be made—a belief held, apparently, by so many people on a primitive level of mind and heart. Quite the reverse. It is charactertistic of genuine love that the couple help one another to keep within the proper limits.

BODILY MATURITY

WE HAVE already spoken more than once of sexual maturity with its symptoms and results. We propose now to consider the relevant processes in their bodily aspects. The sexual glands—in the woman the ovaries arranged in pairs in the abdominal region ; in the man, the testicles and the organs of seminal secretion—grow more and more important in their specific functions as glands concerned with the propagation of life.

The dual function of these glands is well known. On the one hand, they form the germ cells, male and female : these products are passed out *directly*, the ovum through the oviducts into the womb (where if fertilised it becomes embedded) ; the semen through the ducts leading to the seminal vesicle whence, in case of ejection, it passes through the prostate out of the male organ.

On the other hand we have in addition to this direct expulsion an *indirect* flow inwards. In this direction, secretions of various kinds, hormones and others which are of importance to the functions of the system, are absorbed into the bloodstream and distributed throughout the organism, in this way giving rise to all that constitutes the typically male and female. This applies not only to physical sex characteristics but also to those of a psychic nature.

It is generally known that castrated men, or those with underdeveloped sex glands (dystrophia adiposito-genitalis) not only exhibit unmanly or feminine physical characteristics, but their mental attitudes are of corresponding nature. In the same way,

women who have had to have the ovaries removed surgically suffer
a loss of sex characteristics. Maturity brings to both sexes a profound organic change. The glands concerned with internal secretions are mutually dependent, so that the awakening activity of the
sex glands influences the functions of the other secretory glands.

One of the chief effects of the sexual hormones in the organic
field is the development of secondary sexual characteristics, such as
the growth of hair on the body and around the sexual organs, in the
fashion appropriate to each sex ; the development of the breasts in
the female, the growth of a beard and the breaking of the voice
in the male ; also the strengthening, in general, of the specific
bodily forms.

The fundamental symptom of bodily maturity is the capacity
to procreate or to conceive. The first outward sign is the discharge
of semen (pollution) in the case of the boy, and with the girl the first
monthly discharge (menstruation). The frequency of the pollutions
varies according to the physical constitution—once a month would
be an average in the beginning and more frequently at a later
age. It is usually accompanied by dreams of a more or less erotic
nature, often of a very vague character in the earlier stages of
growth.

Many boys experience a severe shock when they become aware,
for the first time, of an erection of the male organ or of a pollution:
as a result of an ultra-puritanical form of sexual education and the
exaggerated scrupulosity so often accompanying it, they are convinced that a serious sin has been committed. That this reaction
has no basis in Christian moral theology (despite isolated examples
of faulty teaching on the subject in earlier ages) can be readily
demonstrated by citing the words of the most authoritative of
Catholic theologians, St. Thomas Aquinas : " . . . what a man does
while he sleeps and is deprived of reason's judgment is not imputed
to him as a sin, as neither are the actions of a maniac or an imbecile.
. . . *Nocturnal pollution is never a sin*, but is sometimes the result of a
previous sin." . . . (*Summa Theologica II–II*, Q. 154, a.5).

And much earlier, St. Athanasius (365) had written : " Will
anyone bring it up against me if mucus flows from my nose or saliva
dribbles from my mouth ? "

An erection is properly to be regarded as a natural reflex, resulting
from a stimulus either from within or without ; it need not even be
a sexual stimulus. It is well known that many men experience an
erection in the morning when the bladder is full and presses upon
the sexual parts. Only when the erection is caused or accompanied
by *conscious* erotic phantasies is there danger of sin ; only if the
phantasies are encouraged with a view to pleasure and self-abuse ;

or, as St. Thomas insists, when the *cause* itself is sinful, can we properly speak of sin.

In the case of girls, regular menstruation does not necessarily follow upon the first manifestation: quite frequently, months—in some cases years—elapse before a second and third menstruation follow or until regularity is established. One hears it said that the periods have been " frightened away " ; for it is more especially girls who are not reconciled to their destiny as women who suffer from this postponement. This situation is especially likely to arise when the girl has not been prepared in good time for what will happen, and is taken by surprise.

To every girl, the first menstruation is a decisive experience ; this follows from the very nature of blood. Blood is life and death ; the flood and the ebb ; love and suffering. Even if the girl is not consciously aware of these implications, there will emerge from the subconscious some dim awareness of the heavy burdens and the profound values which the future may hold in store for her in her rôle of woman and the mate of man.

But when she is not prepared for the responsibilities which now open out before her and knows nothing of the true significance of her natural development, she may suffer a very severe shock the consequence of which may be to inflict serious damage upon her entire development as a woman. It not infrequently happens that she does not feel equal to the dimly envisaged task of woman-hood and seeks to find a refuge in a retreat to the world of childhood : it may then be years before she achieves true maturity, if indeed she ever achieves it.

We have already discussed the problem of delayed maturity. A very late puberty is frequently associated with serious illnesses suffered by the boy or girl in earlier years and leaving behind them a certain loss of vital energy.

An unmarried woman made the following statement: " I was very much alarmed when I experienced my first period. I thought I was ill and confided in our housemaid, for I lacked confidence to go to my mother. The maid told me that now I must undergo an operation ! " Another woman said: " I was taken completely by surprise by the first period and horribly frightened, for I felt sure it must be an illness sent to me as punishment for sexual sins. We had been told that these sins were followed by the most awful illnesses. So I said nothing to anybody. But the next time it could not be concealed. My mother told me that I had reached the age when I had to be ill ; that it could not be helped and was the same for all women. I cried the whole day after that. For years I asked myself why and for what purpose this had to be. Nobody would tell me. I could not get help from my mother. When, at a later age, I began to feel sexual emotions I did not want to have anything to do with sex and thrust it from me. Sometimes, in our gymnastic exercises, I sought pleasure of a sexual nature but when I felt that pleasure coming I suppressed everything, for fear of committing sin."

While in many quarters we find a prudish atmosphere in which the children are not prepared, or not adequately prepared, for later life, there are other families where it is a regular custom to drink the health of a girl who has had her first menstruation. The girl then feels that she is accepted in the circle of the " grown-ups." It is a help in overcoming the painful aspects of the experience.

At a somewhat later stage girls sometimes experience a nocturnal discharge (orgasm), usually during the period when it is promoted by friction from the bindings employed. A girl in her thirties stated that she always tormented herself when she had a period, for fear of such a discharge and tried to avoid it, being afraid even to go to sleep properly ; for she feared it was a forbidden pleasure or even a form of self-abuse. Of the latter she had read in a book of her grandmother's that it was the most terrible of all sins.

In considering menstruation and everything that has to do with it we must never forget that it is not an *illness*, but a natural process. Even if a certain care is advisable during the days in question— especially in the case of delicate girls—we must not make the mistake of treating the matter too seriously. Mothers should make a point of educating their girls in the greatest cleanliness, more especially at the time of the period.

It is important for boys also to pay attention to the cleanliness of sexual parts, for the *glans penis*, in particular, gives rise to a secretion (*smegma*) the removal of which is a part of masculine hygiene and cleanliness. One receives the impression in not a few cases that even a careful washing of the sexual organs could be a danger to spiritual purity. The neglect of proper hygiene is certainly no sign of outstanding chastity. Experience shows that such a " medieval " attitude of hostility towards the body is due to two main causes.

Enmity towards the Body

In the first section of this book under the heading *The Negative Phase*, we have spoken of anxiety in the face of elemental forces emerging from the depths—forces with laws of their own which threaten the supremacy of the conscious mind and seem demoniacal in their unknown potentialities. This anxiety is not concerned solely with the sexual. In the case of a young child it may be manifested for example, with regard to food or sweets. A five-year-old was

sent out to buy a lettuce ; on the way home she met friends playing
in the street and watched them, while she absentmindedly picked off
one lettuce leaf after the other until nothing was left. Then suddenly,
she realised with horror what she had done, or rather what obscure
forces within her had done, for she never had any intention of eating
the lettuce. In similar fashion, children are frequently horrified
when they become aware of the lawless urges within themselves
impelling them to all sorts of naughty actions, although they intend
and wish to be good ; they become aware of what must seem to
them enemy forces within themselves.

The second cause of an inhibiting enmity towards the body lies in
educational methods governed by a fear of these urges. We have
been taught in our religious instruction that it is not permissible,
save in case of necessity, to touch or to look upon the sexual organs ;
but many people, including adults, believe that even in case of
necessity this is sinful—an erroneous idea encouraged by the fact
that in many, even quite recent books of confessional instruction,
we find passages such as this: "Have I touched anything unchaste,
either my own or that of another ? "

This forbidding must be regarded as given for purely pedagogical
reasons ; we must dissociate ourselves from the utterly false and
objectionable mode of expression which suggests that the sexual
organs represent the unchaste element par excellence and are sinful
and in fact evil in themselves.

A wrong sex education gives rise to a wrong attitude towards
sex and to the body in general, and hinders the specific tasks of man
and woman and their entire development. The consequence is
often serious damage to married life, while the disharmony between
body and soul and the inner division of the personality leads to
disturbances over the whole field of human life.

In *Difficulties in Sex Education** we saw that the original relationship of a child to its body is perfectly natural and innocent. It is the
task of sex education to preserve this harmonious state of body and
soul or, if lost, to restore it. When a child, as the result of erroneous
teaching, comes to despise its body and to adopt a negative attitude
towards its physical nature, it has learned to reject its own true
humanity and the consequences will be devastating. In our own
essential being we *are* body just as we are also soul. Each individual
human being *has* a body. This is his property in the most fundamental sense. We are not ears, but we have ears. In the same
fashion we have sexual parts. Like the body as a whole, they form a
fundamental part of man's being. This can and should be looked
upon as a purely objective fact.

*By Baron Frederick von Gagern (*Mercier Press*).

It is right that we should rejoice in our property ; and also that we should joyfully accept the sensuous pleasures provided by the body, in as far as they are in harmony with the moral law and with rightful love. It is amazing how deeply many men and women are convinced that pleasure is sinful in itself. Yet let us look at pain and what a different picture we have ; for surely no one would imagine that an experience of pain, such as toothache, was sinful or forbidden.

The child looks upon his body quite objectively. Unfortunately it happens only too often that " education in purity," incorrectly given, disturbs this wholesome state of things. What was property is now a burden ; and what should be a joy becomes indifferent or even a source of pain. One needs only to think of all the good women whose right relationship to the body has been destroyed by a false education, who regard all bodily sensations of pleasure as sinful and seek to suppress them ; women for whom a normal married life carries with it endless suffering. Nor should we forget the many men to whom an act of loving union brings a sensation of guilt, often of a subconscious nature, followed by suffering—as we know from many an analysis. The damage and disturbance goes deeper. The denial of our fundamental property, the body, carries with it *a wrong attitude towards property in general*, both material and spiritual. By analogy we usually find, in the case of the materialist, an over-valuation of property and, with it, of the body and its care. The man who despises property finds no joy in the gifts sent to him in the spiritual field, and becomes more and more incapable of any deep experience. His life grows empty.

We recognise these patterns in the exaggeration of sensations which is a characteristic of hysterical persons, and again in the withering of personality in cases of obsessional neurosis. The hysterical subject is concerned to convince himself and others how ultra-sensitive he is ; while the other attracts attention by reason of his wooden humourless attitude. The rejection of joy is accompanied by an incapacity for genuine sorrow. Those who live in disharmony of body and soul sometimes admit that they are less disturbed by the loss of those near to them than would have been expected. Their capacity for love and attraction is shallow. In reality they had never at any time really entered into an inward possession of the lost one. Even this does not bring us to the end of the disastrous consequences of this wrong attitude. They reach as far as the last things, the mysteries of religion, of life and death. The " highest good " is also a possession and something that we strive to obtain. But where the urge to possess is not functioning correctly, life must lose its right orientation towards its final aim of eternal salvation, its ultimate fulfilment in a blessedness that cannot fade. This means that life becomes meaningless in its most vital centre. The religious man goes on striving from a sense of duty and law, but his innermost life, his true heart, is not engaged. Inwardly there remains a sense of guilt: a vitally important task has not been fulfilled.

A final word as to a danger too easily arising. In consequence of an unconscious anxiety concerning the loss of possession and of life itself, many people seek, by way of compensation, to hold fast to all that they feel is slipping from them. Following this path they fall into the very thing they want to avoid—the sexual aberration of self-abuse. At the same time, the inward process by which this comes to pass is completely unknown to them. Nevertheless, the sense of guilt is thereby greatly increased and this leads, as we know from experience, to a growing entanglement in sexual difficulties.

Youth Run Wild

In a Munich hospital a girl of thirteen recently gave birth to a baby. When questioned about the paternity, she confessed to having had intercourse with no less than thirteen men in the short period in question. Again, a girl student of twenty-one came to consult a doctor, and, without the least embarrassment, suggested to him that he should carry out an abortion for her. When the doctor made some enquiries, he was told that she had been on a holiday trip and had slept with three different young men, but she did not know the names of any of them, and had never seen them before or since.

We have dealt with the problem of the inhibited: here we are up against the opposite, the total absence of control and even of ordinary decency. Both extremes have one thing in common—the loss of harmony of body and soul and, in consequence, of true humanity. Considered from a fundamental standpoint, the prostitute despises her body just as much as the woman who refuses to accept the idea of the body and its sexuality.

We have already dealt in another work with the wildness and indiscipline of youth to-day and at this point will do no more than add a few words indicating some reasons for this shocking state of things, and suggesting remedies.

In the first place we have the natural *thirst for knowledge* of the child and the adolescent, impelling them to penetrate the mysteries of sex. The more menacing, disordered, and anxiety-ridden the world is, the more urgent becomes the demand for security on the part of the human life-urge. Where a lack of living faith bars the way to a refuge in the field of religion, the individual finds other paths of escape. One of these paths is that of purely rational scientific knowledge: the individual seeks to place solid ground beneath his feet when confronted with the problems and difficulties of life by knowing as much as possible and thus *explaining* the riddles and mysteries that surround him.

The sex instinct can be a source of anxiety and a threat to security: it slumbers, only dimly realised, in the depths of the individual or is awakened through a relationship with another of the opposite sex. It is a mystery and a problem, urging itself upon the individual who feels impelled to explore its true meaning and explain its relationship to himself. The adolescent thus feels driven to find out all he can about this mystery. His curiosity urges him towards experience. If no one helps him along the right lines, he will take the initiative himself. The study of books and dictionaries in the quest of this knowledge is the least harmful aspect of this curiosity. That boys and girls frequently make attempts to view the opposite sex naked is well known. But what does a boy see when he looks at a girl ? Nothing that can answer his questions. The next step is that he feels impelled to take his investigations a stage further. The playful mutual examination which takes place amongst children in the well-known " doctor game " is relatively harmless ; but, at a later age, the matter becomes serious. Young people will often not shrink from " trying things out " in a sexual sense ; then we get actual intercourse, either amongst those of a like age or with older friends, boys or girls, who are apt to take a special delight in " initiating " the innocent younger ones. Sexual curiosity in itself is a natural thing ; but such crass behaviour as we have suggested, with its gross violation of modesty, indicates a deplorable lack of that sense of shame which should act as a barrier, defending what is, in reality a holy thing. We see that the task of education, despite all good intentions, has failed.

The danger is increased through a factor in the subconscious, an element of anxiety peculiarly threatening because it is not known. It is this fear of the unknown that, in many cases, drives adolescents to such adventures as we have indicated, in the hope of coming to grips with this unknown and understanding it. But, as history teaches us, attack is not always the best defence ; sometimes it leads to utter destruction. Not a few adolescents destroy themselves in their efforts to escape from what they feel to be a threat. After all, love itself is the most obvious regulator of sexuality. Let us not forget that in the first half of puberty this aesthetic-sensual love is not yet awakened, and that in the following years *eros* and *sexus* develop independently of one another without forming a unity. It will then be clear that in these early years of the maturing process the activity of instinct in the absolute sense will be stronger than during the approaching years of young manhood. This is another factor lending impetus to undisciplined sexuality with all its aberrations.

The forces impelling youth to plunge into a wild sexuality are supplemented from many other quarters. Amongst these is the element of pleasurable excitement : this increases in power in proportion to the lack of real joy in the life of the adolescent. There can be no doubt at all that those young people are the most endangered whose lives are lacking in the experience of genuine values. In the case of sexual experiences entered upon from curiosity, the element of spiritual love is driven into the background, and, in consequence, the affair acquires an almost wholly animal character. Intercourse of this sort can be justly described as " self-abuse aided by another person "—a description often given by the parties themselves. In passing, it should be noted that the *doing of something forbidden* often imparts a peculiar zest to such affairs, and helps to destroy the last defences and to banish shame. It is well known that young people who have been brought up very strictly and separated from others, lose self-control the most easily when once they taste freedom: they have always *been* guarded and have never learned to guard themselves. The temptation to do forbidden things is likely to persist throughout the whole period of youth. Understandably enough this attitude is peculiarly strong in the oppositional phase of puberty.

When we speak of depraved and abandoned children, as we very well may, we lay ourselves open to a quite logical question : who is responsible ? Young people are not naturally depraved. What has happened to bring about this shocking state of things ? It is we grown-ups who ought to beat our breasts and question ourselves—we who are so quick to denounce the "youth of to-day." Why have parents not catered for their children, instead of letting them go down to ruin ? Moreover, do we not find signs of moral depravity in the case of the very children who have been carefully— too carefully—protected ?

What is here in question is no mere outward discipline, but the sense of being inwardly secure in genuine parental love. In this way, the child gains confidence in the world and in itself, developing that feeling of security that enables it to face and overcome the threats surging upwards from the depths. Parents who have succeeded in establishing this atmosphere of confidence will find that the children come to them with their problems and questions about life and receive satisfying answers from them. The dangers resulting from errant curiosity are then removed.

The loved child is the child with confidence in its own value, and, consequently, with the courage and strength to take up the fight against all hostile powers, within or without. Every human being needs this love—has, indeed, a right to it. The child denied adequate love will, later in life, as adolescent or even as grown-up man, yearn for what was missing. He will confront the world with an unpaid bill—will strive to *get* love ; and this yearning may very well drive him into the arms of some pseudo-lover, some poor substitute for the real thing, some encounter in which the partners *act as if they loved one another*. No real satisfaction comes of such substitute satisfaction, any more than it can derive from onanism. The hungry man rises from the table as hungry as when he sat down expecting a nourishing meal ; and his next step will be to seek further pseudo-satisfaction in other similar false relationships.

We must not overlook the fact that the young person who has not been confirmed in his self-esteem through a right parental love experiences a *confirmation of his value* through intercourse with the opposite sex : he realises that he possesses a power and a value sought after by his partner. This experience of self-esteem combined with a desire for individuality and a craving to be manly, which he believes to be satisfied through such encounters, is without doubt a powerful stimulus to the exercise of his sexual powers.

We have already mentioned that an essential cause of the ruin of so many young people is to be found in inadequate love and care on the part of the parents. In such cases, it is not at all surprising that the marriage of the parents is found to be lacking in love and not rightly lived ; for lack of love towards the child is usually based upon an incapacity for giving love. Uneasy and emotionally bankrupt marriages create a milieu highly injurious to the children and calculated to thrust them into sexual depravity.

Exaggerated sexual curiosity and precosity are often accounted for by the fact that children have opportunities in their home life to observe sexual intercourse between adults. If it is a case of the parents—which can hardly be avoided when children of all ages up to fourteen share the parents' bedroom— this can have another effect, namely to arouse disgust and a feeling of strong protest, not only against the sexual in itself but against the parents in particular. Other experiences may serve only to sharpen curiosity ; for example, bad films, pornographic literature, the letting of rooms to couples regardless of moral consequences, etc.

Is Continence Injurious?

Priests frequently ask a doctor questions in order to enable them to give firm and well founded answers to those who may challenge them on points of morality and law. One of these questions of interest to educators and to all young people concerns continence. Is it injurious to health to abstain from every form of sexual activity during the period between sexual maturity and marriage? Is such activity necessary for the development of personality ? Or, on the contrary, is continence more calculated to promote health and moral and spiritual development ? Here we seek deliberately to answer this question not from a purely moral or religious standpoint, but primarily from the medical and psychological angles.

We have spoken elsewhere of premarital intercourse and its background.* Such intercourse is not necessary as a sort of safety valve for the accumulated secretions of the body, as is often believed by young people. The natural emissions taking place during the night serve this purpose. On the other hand, premarital sex life is a grave danger to physical health, as is witnessed by the extremely high proportions of young people infected with venereal diseases. Nor is it without danger in a psychological sense. This is especially true of the woman, whose inner harmony is even more seriously threatened than that of the man when she gives herself without genuine lasting devotion. The immediate results are uneasiness of mind and sensations of guilt, often of an unconscious character. The free development of personality is inhibited.

Let us not forget the conditions essential to a wholehearted and complete union of man and woman in body and mind. We take our stand upon the ontological conception of the human entity, in which the body is the habitation of the soul and the soul's means of expression. On the physical side, the act of becoming one in the flesh presupposes that the loving couple are one in heart and soul— or at least wish to be one. This attitude of the mind is active and dynamic ; as a consequence, it insists upon the basic condition of a wholehearted love : namely the demand for an eternal love . . . (we will love one another until death do us part) . . . and the claim to an exclusive love . . . (to thee alone will I give myself in wholehearted love). These two pledges alone create the foundation of spiritual union, and form also the right basis for the sacrament of marriage on its spiritual side. Thus the vow of marriage—if this vow be true and fulfilled—affords the sole guarantee of the mental and spiritual conditions needful for a harmonious union. Unions which do not fulfil or only partially fulfil these conditions are in contradiction to the harmony of body and soul ; thus, in a certain sense, they are not *true*. Truth and untruth are dependent on the degree of love.

The organic development of personality, supposes the harmony of body and soul. The numerous attempts made by young people to experiment in sexual unions not based upon any real foundation of

* *Difficulties in Married Life*, by Baron Frederick von Gagern (*Mercier Press*).

love have always proved to be errors and have not brought about the development often expected by the partners. This is more especially the case with women, because the consequences are deeper and more damaging, a fact linked up with their closer connection with the life of the body and with nature herself. Nevertheless, when a genuine love prompts the act of union, it is certainly possible that inner development can take place, but we can assume that this is due to the love which is felt and not to the sexual act. The growth of personality that may, in such a case, take place would as a rule be greater if the couple refrained from the completion of their union from the motive of their mutual love.

The practice of love, including its physical exercise, is calculated to promote the development of personal life, if it is carried out under the conditions we have explained. But when the needful conditions are not present, sexual relationships can be looked upon—if we take a really fundamental viewpoint—as a species of auto-eroticism often little better than plain self-abuse, and therefore an abnormal sexual act by means of which no development of the individual can be expected. As regards continence, the really decisive question is not the act, but the fundamental attitude. Just as obedience based upon fear is devoid of moral value, while the obedience of love can be a step in free self-develoment, so continence is far from being a moral act when due to fear of disease or of punishment as a sin ; but, if based upon a high ideal of chastity, it is the act of courageous youth. Again, continence is sometimes practised because of a shrinking from the personal surrender involved in wholehearted love, and anxiety in the face of the deep instinctive forces in personality. In such an attitude these forces are not transcended but merely suppressed—sex is, so to speak, rejected and every sensual impulse is crushed. This is pure negation, a refusal to face the tasks of real life, and, as such, is an immoral state of mind. To speak of chastity in this connection, when we should say *suppression*, is a sheer mockery of the truth and a trifling with conscience itself. True chastity, with or without continence, promotes the development of personality. Abstinence without chastity can, on the other hand, be thoroughly injurious. It has been described in *New Problems in Medical Ethics (First Series)* as " an open door to neurosis."

In conclusion: premarital continence has no injurious consequences, either mental or spiritual. It is not intercourse which furthers development but *love itself*. Continence without true chastity is not a moral achievement ; it is either a mere suppression or a means of escape. But character can be strengthened and the growth of personality promoted by a chaste continence, a fact demonstrated convincingly by many of the celibates in the Church.

Moral Help for the Young

Mature chaste personalities will always seek to guard and preserve a right order in life. Therefore our educators and priests, although surrounded by the disorder of the day, will continue to find their primary task in forming and preserving the harmonious development of body and soul in our children and awakening the ideal of chastity in their minds. We will make no great use of materialistic arguments—such as the danger of sexual diseases—but concentrate on arousing a positive will to chastity. With this in view, it is vital that the significance of chastity as a moral *value* should be experienced and understood. How can this be done? The most important thing is to perceive the value of sex itself ; to understand that it is not something to be ashamed of, that it is neither evil nor lacking in value. It will then become the interest of the growing child to preserve this value in true chastity. He will realise that it is placed in his charge, that it is his duty to guard this gift, at once so valuable and so easily damaged.

If this kind of influence is not begun until the period of puberty, it will be necessary to clear away a number of false ideas and wrong elements in training. This involves not only such as have to do with the depreciation of sex but also the whole complex of false notions encouraging premarital relationships. The pseudo-halo of heroic vitality which often clings about the head of the Don Juan type must be stripped away, leaving the subject with the consciousness that he is not sexually normal. What is he really ? A young man who has failed to transcend puberty on the mental and moral level and is ceaselessly seeking to compensate his unconscious sense of inferiority by conquests amongst the females of his environment. Abundance of material for a convincing analysis of such a type will be found in the classic case of Casanova : this famous character possessed a history of marked neurosis and was, fundamentally, incapable of love.

The adolescent should be guided and formed through the example of those who possess a true sense of chastity, both inside and outside married life. He should carefully consider whether he wants his partner, the mother of his children, to be a controlled or a dissolute character. How can a man find the capacity for sacrifice so often needed in marriage if he does not learn beforehand in the school of self-discipline ? In order to acquire a true sense of chastity as an attitude of mind and an aid to the high demands of love, all those things are needful that we have already discussed in detail in our book *Difficulties in Sex Education.* A reformation of the existing state of affairs is urgently necessary if the mental and spiritual health of our young people, and hence of the nation, is not to be more and more undermined. We have to build a better and more solid foundation. We must summon all our forces to overcome the moral weakening and corruption of the rising generation and provide it with effective aid. This is now recognised by authoritative leaders, who have called for a crusade to save our young people. For example, we have the lecture series arranged in connection with the *Jugendschutzwochen*. These provide intensive study courses for one week, on how to protect and aid young people, with lectures designed to arouse parents to a deeper sense of their responsibilities and encourage them to tackle the problem of sex instruction personally on the right lines. In most cases, however, the parents are in need of enlightenment themselves as to the true meaning of love and sex. They need to learn, for example, that their own sex relations do not represent a legalised form of immorality, a widely held view due to wrong education—sometimes on the part of priests. These weekly lecture series are also directed towards young people with a view to helping them to make up for something, at least, of what should have been done for them by their parents or guardians. The aim of the series is to throw a clear light upon the true meaning of love, marriage, and sex ; to demonstrate that body and soul form a unity and that the sexual element finds its inner significance as the expression of genuine love ; and to provide from this stand-point right answers to the ever-recurring problem of premarital relations.

Attempts are now being made on all sides to foster a great renewal of marriage. Marriage courses have been held with outstanding success ; but such things are hardly more than drops of water on hot bricks. Yet, we may hope that marriages thus influenced may proceed on right lines and form cells for the propagation of healthy moral life. Many branches of Catholic activity are gradually becoming fired with the ideal of reforming and revivifying married life. Nevertheless it is a source of shame to us that so little interest is aroused in the masses. Bourgeois smugness and inertia triumph so easily over our sense of responsibility. It is of the first importance that priests, educators, and all persons in charge of the young should make a careful study of the problems connected with marriage and with the work of educational advisory bodies. A large portion of the troubles associated with family life could be alleviated in this way, the most obstinate cases being left to the consideration of specialists. We are glad to note that considerable progress has already been made along these lines.

In all these things, we must never forget that it is useless to wax indignant about " the youth of to-day" and their dissolute conduct.

We have to accept the facts as they are. Twenty years ago it was girls of eighteen years old or thereabouts who were the objects of pursuit on the part of young fellows; to-day it is the twelve- and even eleven-year-olds who arouse this kind of interest. We know, too, that it is very often the girls who make the advances—even at such an early age. For these reasons, it is most important that, by the age of ten, some foundation of genuine values should be laid—something better than is supplied by the cinema, the comic papers, cheap illustrated journals and novelettes. The development of higher values linked with the ideal side of sex, counteracts the over-valuation of the crude sex element already apparent, and thus provides a real aid to the boy or girl. We have already touched upon the important service that can be rendered by youth groups in this field. The provision of ideals and values appealing to the higher sex personality of the young will always be a significant factor in overcoming the troubles and difficulties of adolescence. In this connection, a word with respect to the use of spare time in the evenings may be useful. It is far too often the case that young people, especially in the absence of any organisation to help them, have no real home where they can meet in comfort and with a feeling of freedom. They drift to cafes, cinemas, and other undesirable places. The dangers are too obvious to require comment.

It would be a splendid thing if we had youth hostels and meeting places everywhere, where young people could find recreation, games, and company of a wholesome kind. Priests and other representatives of authority should remain discreetly in the background. The more naturally young people can meet—possibly under some supervision from a trustworthy older boy or girl—the less will be the danger of undesirable happenings.

If we have the opportunity of a real personal talk with an adolescent who is in difficulties, this forms the best possible starting point in giving help. But we must avoid moralising, for this causes the modern boy or girl to " dry up ", and will destroy our points of contact. It is quite possible, on the basis of a purely human and man-to-man attitude, to say all that is needful to convince the other. A most useful question is simply: " Do you really know yourself, *what* it is you want ? " He is now forced to examine himself. He feels confirmed in his desire for love—not in itself wrong—and begins to feel confidence. This can be followed up by the more penetrating question: " Have you found what it was you were seeking, and are you satisfied ? " It is more than likely that after some hesitation and self-examination he will find himself forced to admit that the path he is taking in the search for love does not give him real satisfaction—is not in fact the right path. This leads naturally to the question as to what is the path that will give real satisfaction. Pursuing this line of thought, he can be led to understand how necessary it is that the heart itself should have its place in any true and satisfying love. He is now on the way to take a decisive step, and to grasp the significance of chastity.

The power of false ideas about sex is often disastrous when a young boy or girl is brought face to face with the realities of fatherhood and motherhood, without right preparation—even when the parents themselves are in question : a severe crisis may be brought about in many cases. A lad of sixteen told me: " I despise my parents' bodies. I feel disgust, now that I know how children are brought into being." An eighteen-year-old said: " I felt overwhelmed with shame for my parents when I saw that my mother expected a baby. I could not have believed it possible that either of them could commit unchaste acts." And a young woman of thirty said : " I could not look my parents in the face. The world seemed full of lies and deception. Even to-day I cannot bear to be in the same room with them, listening to the radio, if the broadcast programme touches upon love." Yet this same girl had had experiences of a sexual nature herself.

We can attempt to make it clear that the bodies of the parents are the workshops of God, where is performed the wonderful work of producing, through the contact of ovum and semen, the living entity that is a new human being, endowed with an immortal soul. Thus God blesses the act of love by enacting the miracle that brings spirit to the world of nature. Father and mother are obeying the law of God by being fruitful and multiplying. And through this obedience the child is brought into being ; first sheltered in the mother's womb until, through her pain and suffering, the new creature is delivered. A new child of God is born, a new pilgrim on the road to Heaven. In this way an experience which often disturbs young people deeply and destroys their relationship to their parents can be lifted up to a higher level and interpreted in the light of true values. When the opportunity seems suitable, we can go further and say something about the abuse of sex in general, pointing out, perhaps, that even the abused and prostituted body still remains a wonderful instrument through which God can perform His works ; but one must know how to seek and find. Let us imagine a valuable monstrance displayed in a jeweller's window. A first glance reveals what are obviously costly jewels and golden settings. A more understanding eye may perceive the beauty of the work involved and value it artistically. But, finally, yet another and more profound vision will penetrate to the inner nature of the piece displayed and will recognise in it the glorification of God on the part of faithful men. It may often happen that one does not reach the centre of the disturbance by *conscious* observation. There may be inward relationships of an *unconscious* nature with father or mother such as the Oedipus situation (Freud). Such factors are for the most part so deeply embedded in the subconsious mind that the crisis can hardly be overcome without the aid of psychoanalysis.

Last but not least in the methods of approach to youth is the *religious* aspect. Some of the difficulties in this task have already been touched upon. Those who have had to do with boys of, say 14 to 17, learning to be skilled mechanics or bootmakers or what not, will not need to be told how closed are their minds against religious influences, more especially during this period. Religious teaching and maxims are apt to rebound from their minds like peas from a tank ; their attitude is one of opposition and no sound foundation has been laid. Many religious instructors take the view that one should lay the emphasis rather on the Christian way of life than on doctrine and belief. My own view is that it is important, especially at the above mentioned ages, to concentrate upon an easily grasped and practical training in *virtue*, in the positive sense. Unfortunately it is almost universally found that far too little stress is laid upon this aspect of life, and far too much upon all sorts of negatives—you must *not* do this or that ! It is of the first importance that adolescents should be brought to a realisation of the *meaning of life* in so personal a fashion that each individual may perceive something of this meaning in his own experience. With this as a beginning, the way is paved for further self-realisation. A knowledge of modern psychology will offer many opportunities of building up character from within outwards, instead of inviting the opposition of the young by imposing something upon them from outside.

When we find that a barrier has been put up against our religious ideas—as is so often the case with young people to-day—it is best to abandon the direct approach. In its place, we can stress the effort to live a good and noble life as the task most suitable to youth. The effort to recognise what is good, to further it, and to imitate it ; to perceive the beautiful, to enjoy it and to pursue it, with a view to ourselves becoming beautiful characters ; to experience the value of truth, its place in our own lives as a guiding principle ; and to grow in inward unity, in harmony with ourselves, with the outside world and the world above, in an all-embracing personal love for others. If we lead young people along this path, it cannot be long before they will meet Him who is the Way and the Life.

Part III

SELF-ABUSE AND ITS PSYCHOLOGICAL BACKGROUND

APPROACHING THE PROBLEM

WE HAVE nothing outstandingly new to put forward in this study. But in the interests of a better understanding of this problem, we seek to gather together certain points of view. Practical experience in the consulting room of a psychotherapeutic practitioner makes it clear that it is imperatively necessary to deal with the old problem of self-abuse (onanism) from a modern angle. The helplessness with which parents, educators and especially priests—together, needless to say, with all those who suffer through it—face this problem, is so striking that we can justly speak of a real tragedy. The measures taken by the uninformed to combat this evil are usually useless and are often quite grotesque. The spiritual trouble and the suffering which overtake large numbers of people through this habit cry out for some remedy. Many priests know this well and are filled with anxiety about the young sufferers who slip away from their control and often end by leaving the Church altogether. Good spiritual directors have recognised, in practice, that the problem of self-abuse cannot be dealt with either by laxity or by a stern and rigorous attitude. This approach is apt to lead to the exact opposite of what is desired. Through the experience of the confessional, many priests have been moved to change their own position, but do not feel sure as to the correctness of their course, for the new scientific knowledge in this field, which forms the basis of a different attitude, is only gradually permeating official circles. The relevant literature giving advice and aid is still far too little known.

I should like to select for special mention a little book by Alois Gügler (a priest and educator) entitled: *Die Erziehliche Behandlung jugendlicher männlicher Onanisten* (The Educational Treatment of Youthful Male Onanists). Use has been made, in the following, of his extremely careful work and extensive knowledge and his many references to literature, although I do not find myself able to agree with all that he says. Since the work is now out of print, I feel it a duty not only to draw attention to it, but also to quote a few passages. A considerable number of articles dealing with the problem of self-abuse have appeared in the *Katechetische Blätter*, a periodical of value in the study of youth problems (see Appendix).

It is my hope that my own contribution here will serve to further a new and better understanding of the spiritual needs of mature and maturing young people and may be an aid in tackling their difficulties. The material of depth psychology will here be of fundamental significance. It will lead us to new lines of thought.

The Sin of Onan

In the thirty-eighth chapter of Genesis we have, in the first ten verses, the well-known biblical reference to onanism : " And Her the first-born of Juda, was wicked in the sight of the Lord: and was slain by him. Juda therefore said to Onan his son : Go into thy brother's wife and marry her, that thou mayst raise seed to thy brother. He knowing that the children should not be his, when he went into his brother's wife, spilled his seed upon the ground, lest children should be born in his brother's name. And therefore the Lord slew him, because he did a detestable thing." (*Gen.* 38 : 7-10).

The question of the precise nature of the sin committed by Onan, which carried with it the death penalty, has often been discussed. A primitive mode of thought, near to materialism, perceives only the actual *act*. In that case, the sin is that of the *coitus interruptus*, the breaking off of the sexual act, so that the semen does not enter the natural channel. Under the influence of this idea, many theologians have used the term onanism for the *coitus interruptus*.

The evangelical theologian, Gunkel, takes a more profound view and considers that the sin lay in the motives of selfishness and jealousy that prevented Onan from fulfilling his duty to his brother's wife, according to the levitical law: he sinned against the demands of justice and love. Others take the view that Onan sinned in both the above ways ; and F. Hamp points out that deception also played a part in his condemnation : the manner in which Onan sought to prevent conception doubled his guilt.

According to the Jewish mode of thought, their laws were always the laws of God ; thus, from this angle the sin of Onan can be summarised as follows : it was an act of rebellion against the express law of God; a clear case of *non serviam*. It was also an egoistic act, a sin against the fundamental law of love, since he wanted to deprive his elder brother of a male heir—possibly in order himself to inherit the property ; it was an act of mendacity and deception for Onan pretended to fulfil the law, while cunningly evading it ; in order to carry into effect his evil intentions, he practised *coitus interruptus*, thus committing a further sin by offending against the inner reality of the sexual act.

In my view it is not justifiable to regard the last of these points as the chief sin. The basic factor in an act of sin remains the evil *intention* behind the act, the decision to turn away from God ; the act is the outward and visible expression of the evil mind.

The use of the term " onanism " to denote sexual self-abuse can be related to the act of Onan in the following points : the dynamic forces of the soul were not directed outwards in love towards others, but inward towards the self ; the secrecy of the act preserved an outward appearance of conformity with the law, while the spirit was turned in the opposite direction ; and, finally, the self-abuse itself offended against the inner reality of the sexual act.

The Definitions of Onanism (Self-Abuse)

As we have seen, onanism strictly speaking—that is, as related to Onan—is the act of the *coitus interruptus*, the sexual act broken off before the semen can enter the woman's body. The term is often employed by theologians in this sense, and self-abuse is referred to as *molities*, *pollutio*, or *masturbatio*. But, in modern literature on the subject, the term " onanism " has become established in the sense of self-abuse. The term *masturbatio*, referring to the use of the hand, is also made use of, more especially with reference to a certain type of female self-abuse ; but this is vague and unsatisfactory, since obviously the hand is not always used.

Havelock Ellis sought for a better term, one that would express the real *nature* of self-abuse, and made use of the word " auto-erotism." E. Bleuler employed the term " autism," which might, however, apply to many other things. *Ipsation* has also been used. M. Hodan defines onanism as, " the production of sensations of sexual pleasure by means of conscious or unconscious actions in relation to one's own body " ; involuntary nocturnal emissions were not included.

Alois Gügler has defined onanism as, " an unnaturally produced excitement of the sexual organs, usually carried out by the individual himself as a result of the egocentric and weak character of the subject, and related to the tendency to seek pleasure and satisfaction " ; and, in another place, he writes: " Onanism is a solitary voluntary, conscious, self-produced genital excitation with its accompanying relief, not carried out under the pressure of necessity, and is a symptom of individually varying dispositions, experiences, and life-attitudes of the personality as a whole " ; while, in yet a third passage, he says " Onanism is an excitation of the sexual parts, carried out on one's own person, and in such a fashion as to exclude the natural function of reproduction."

It is, however, a fact that young people of both sexes not infrequently practise mutual self-abuse, or self-abuse in groups. The latter is more common with boys, who like to exhibit their manliness to one another, while with girls the mutual practice is more frequently found. This latter must be sharply distinguished from lesbianism, for the partner is regarded as taking the place of a dimly realised but as yet non-existent male lover. As soon as a real male comes on the scene, the mutual self-abuse will cease ; but with lesbian practices this is not the case. The question may certainly be put with some justification : is not the kind of inter-course with a member of the opposite sex which then ensues, itself no more than a form of mutual self-abuse? Inwardly regarded, is not this, too, more a case of self-satisfaction than of a genuine love with the devotion that arises from it ? On the other hand, it is certain that the mutual self-abuse of girls may be classed as the beginning of a not as yet practicable fulfilment through a real partner in love ; a beginning that, at a later date, can be com-pleted with the male partner.

The second point in Gügler's definition is open to criticism in the use of the term " conscious," because onanism, especially in the case of children, occurs only very rarely without the modifying influence of the unconscious, since it depends upon factors in the mind. Of this we shall speak when we come to consider the causes of onanism. Nor can I agree with the term " voluntary, " for it is usually inaccurate, on account of the same factors. Do we not know that there are many who practise onanism against their express intention and will? The consent ultimately given, in these cases, represents a surrender under a pressure which limits the operation of free will.

Anticipating the insight that we are seeking in the further progress of this study, I should like to put forward a definition. Onanism is sexual excitement and satisfaction sought either alone or with others as a means to procure pleasure or relief, usually as a reaction brought about by motives in the unconscious. It is in opposition to the natural function of the sexual organs, properly used as the bodily expression of love between the two sexes : it is thus in its essence an egocentric urge opposed to the urge of love.

The Essential Nature of Self-Abuse

The above definition makes it clear that the fundamental roots of onanism are to be found in the dynamic nature of the instinctive urges. In our book *Difficulties in Life* we have examined in some detail the two oppposed forces dominating the direction of our life-energies. One of these impels us to the fulfilment of life and is directed towards the greatest possible degree of completion and perfection ; we have called it the urge of love, in the most general sense. In it we seek the *other*, and through this search find our own true selves. The opposed urge is that towards egocentricity. This is the basic symptom of all regression. It represents a pursuit of the ego, in the superficial and peripheral sense. On the other hand, the upward struggle which attempts to realise true manhood and personality, enriches the whole nature, promotes the growth of love, and the overcoming of the tyranny of egocentricity. We must not fall into the error of failing to distinguish between true self-love and false egotism.

A man finds fulfilment and satisfaction when he throws his whole being into his life-tasks, inspired by love ; when his heart, mind, and all his powers are thus devoted. He will find himself when he loses himself. But when he seeks his own satisfaction, his life will remain empty and unsatisfactory. This is true even when the egoism is indirect. When a woman says: " I will do anything for my husband, if only he loves me," she reveals a disguised form of egoism, the falsity of which is seen when it is proved more powerful than real love. If I love someone because I want to be loved *myself*, instead of giving love in order to further the interests of the loved one, to make him (or her) happy, satisfied and fulfilled—even perhaps to the point of giving freedom from a tie—that is egoism and a form of self-abuse through the agency of another.

Is there not a contradiction in the use of the term self-abuse in relation to a partner ? By no means : for it is the individual himself who seeks and procures his satisfaction. The partner is used as a means to an end. The relationship is very close to that of mutual self-abuse. There is no spiritual contact with the partner ; the tie is imaginary or it is a case of self-projection in phantasy. The contact is unreal and peripheral.

What Is Onanism ?

Sexual pleasure, in its highest perfection and complete distinction from the merely animal, rests upon the full union of man and woman, the two becoming one. Body and soul participate in the sexual act, which is an expression of devotion, ultimate surrender, and transfusion of the individual. The couple strive towards the perfect fulfilment of the ideal WE, venturing to give up their egos in this new ideal, to receive them again enriched and fulfilled.

They are aware of the gift of pleasure which is bestowed upon them while thus striving. They seek it and rejoice in it. Yet, even more, each seeks to cherish the other with whom union is sought. This enduring and cherishing love becomes an irrevocable part of their lives ; it is a symbol and expression of the deep reality and fulfilment of the relationship. But if the satisfaction of the ego stands in the foreground, the act of love is deprived of its deepest roots; it becomes empty and sinks to the level of a misuse of the partner and of marriage itself. In the most literal sense, it is *abusus matrimonii*. The pleasure sought in onanism has no meaning and no promise of fulfilment, for it is remote from love, the WE relationship of true sexual life. The urge is directed towards self and not outwards towards a loved person, and is thus opposed to the fundamental urge of man and woman, with all its far-reaching consequences Here is nothing of devotion, care or responsibility. By its very nature sex is concerned with *another* and without this other is lacking in all truth and reality ; it becomes no more than a flight from reality and its demands, not the least of which is the venture of love. There can be no partnership in egocentricity. The world of phantasy is brought in to fill the void. But this world cannot give back the self, enriched and fulfilled, as in real love. The pleasure thus becomes increasingly unreal, unsatisfactory, and superficial. The more it is pursued the less can there be satisfaction. An urge to repeat the onanism will ensue, and finally its tyranny will be established, and we have compulsory onanism.

Yet, despite everything, there is in onanism an attempt at the formation of a kind of reality. The failure to procure what is sought after is not, by itself, enough to bring about the abandonment of the habit. Further attempts will be made to see if, after all, the impossible cannot be achieved ; through a greater use of phantasy and an improved technique, it is hoped the goal may be reached. In this way many find themselves caught in the trap of habitual onanism, from which escape is difficult. Since no phantasy can replace the absent partner, the sexual loses all its character and we have nothing left save a sensation devoid of meaning.

We have already spoken of the change in the relationship to the body brought about by love. If beforehand it could be said that we *have* a body, it is felt in the sexual act of love that we *are* a body. In onanism the impossible is attempted—to have a body and to be a body ; for here two forms come into contact: the sexual pole and the pole of consciousness. The act of love creates a world of harmony and is an agent in promoting development ; in the practice of onanism, the body sets up a barrier beyond which there is nothing but emptiness, and within which the individual is isolated. He cannot transcend this barrier, break through, or climb over it, to make contact with a real person with whom he might establish a real relationship ; he is left with the impossible task of transcending himself. He feels, however, that this effort, contrary as it is to the realities of life, is a contradiction in itself, a falsity which must fill him with anxiety and a consciousness of guilt. For the practice of self-abuse always leaves untouched that portion of the personality which is concerned with giving and devotion, having been implanted by nature as part of the impulse which impels the quest for a partner. Confined to the self, this is empty of all meaning. The sense of guilt that derives from this is wholly intangible, and thus all the more a source of anxiety.

To sum up we may say : the nature of onanism is determined by its meaninglessness. The practice leads to isolation and inward division. It contradicts the truth of life and love itself and is an offence against the natural task of life, and the forward movement of vital forces beyond the ego. In place of this, the onanist regresses to a primitive sexual stage centred in self. Such an attitude of disharmony is a fault which must arouse anxiety and feelings of guilt and act as a hindrance to the development of the individual. How far these statements apply to all forms of onanism or only to certain types, could be determined only by a special investigation.

Perversion

The literature of the present day is divided as to whether onanism should be regarded as a " fragmentary perversion " (H. Kunz) or as an " original perversion " (v. Hattingberg). N. Boss does not look upon it as perversion at all, but as, " a mere technique for bringing about a sexual orgasm. " Ernst Speer, in his last book, *Das Einswerden von Mann und Weib* (1952), is sharply opposed to the view that self-abuse is a perversion.

" Freud still believed," he writes, " that self-abuse was a survival of an infantile stage, a continuance of childish bad habits in playing with the organs in question. This cannot be accepted for a moment. The habit is a possibility, persisting throughout life, one of the means of procuring sexual relief. The others are pollution and sexual intercourse." In another place, he speaks even more plainly : " Under no circumstances can we regard self-abuse as a form of perversion ; the latter is a diseased development of a faulty kind, or an error in development ; but self-abuse is a function open to the healthy man, one which he may employ until an advanced age."

Von Gebsattel relates the anthropological theory of perversion to the love-pattern of personal life ; he believes that the real meaning of perverse acts and experiences is to be sought in the deformation of a normal love-pattern which has been destroyed. If we follow this line of thought, we have to believe that a single act contrary to what is normal and right constitutes perversity. But psychiatry tells us that we should not speak of perversity unless the character of the person in question exhibits a *lasting* natural disposition towards perverse acts. This could not be said of isolated acts of self-abuse. Gebsattel believes that all genuine perversity, regarded from the psychiatric angle, can be characterised by an addiction which forms the sex-pattern of the individual, such as we find in the case of established

onanism.   Accordingly, he does not place either the self-abuse
of puberty or that of those who turn to it from necessity (being
deprived of other outlets by external causes) in the category of
addictions and thus of perversions.   But is it not really a case of
degree ?   Even with isolated acts, we must reckon with egocentricity,
the pursuit of selfish ends, even if we do not speak of addiction ?

In my own view, one must distinguish between perverse acts
as expressions of an attitude forming part of the subject's character,
and acts which may occur in an isolated fashion and are, in themselves, perverse but not embedded in the sex-pattern.   The former
one might call downright perversion, while the latter are symptoms
of a wayward nature.

One could then say that perversions are strongly marked practices
divergent from normal sexuality, having the character of addictions,
and resulting from a personality with an established perverse sexual
disposition.   In this category we can place the psychopathological
forms of homosexuality, fetishism, sodomy, sadism and masochism
and intermingled types ; we may include also established onanism,
for it can be continued after marriage when normal sexual activity
is possible.

Under the head of wayward *symptoms* we may include more or
less passing divergences of the sexual energies, directed towards the
self instead of towards another person.   They are to be noted when a
regression is not of a lasting nature, but the product of temporary
circumstances and liable to change with these ; there may be no
established disposition of character of a perverse nature—nothing
more than an undue liability to be influenced.   Also to be included
are the self-abuse of puberty and onanism from necessity.   We may
speak, too, of such symptomatic perversity in cases where the
self-abuse is not sexual but of a mental or spiritual nature.   Here,
too, we may find addiction.

I cannot agree with Speer that onanism can be put on the same
level with involuntary emissions or even with normal sexual intercourse, as a form of natural activity.   Considered from a psychic
viewpoint, there is surely a basic difference between the orientation
of the sexual life urge towards self and its expression in union with
another in real bodily love.

SYMPTOMS RELATED TO SELF-ABUSE

" MY FEELINGS of self-pity were certainly a form of self-abuse," said
a woman patient who, when a child, had been accustomed to
inflict injuries on herself in order, as she admitted, to enjoy afterwards the sensation of self-pity.   In a natural state of affairs, this

child would have sought love from her parents ; but this was denied, and she endeavoured to provoke her father and mother into offering pity as a species of substitute love. Reactions of this type are not uncommon in the case of children who feel they do not get enough attention ; they often do all sorts of naughty things to obtain at least a negative attention in the shape of punishment.   In the case of this little girl, her cunning attempts to enlist her parents' interest and love proved useless ; she then drew back into herself, lost spirit, and bestowed upon herself the pity the parents had denied.

We find here an example of a typical inward process of a kind likely to lead to self-abuse on the mental level.   When this girl grew older, she gave up her practice of self-inflicted injuries and the accompanying self-pity, and began to practice actual self-abuse, which continued until her tie with the parents—which was negative and oppositional—was broken.

Doctors in psychotherapeutic practice meet with quite a large number of more or less similar forms of self-abuse on a mental level, all of which have a clear relationship to physical self-abuse, sometimes in the sense that where the one exists the other is absent, as in the above case. A few words on this problem will not be out of place.

Self-Abuse on the Mental Level

One day I was told by a girl student who had long been given to self-abuse: " Since I threw myself, with all my energy, into scientific work and found satisfaction in that, I have ceased to practice self-abuse. I am aware, however, that the outwardly visible work I produce is nothing more than a different form of self-abuse—in fact mental and spiritual onanism." Perhaps the girl was right because when she had exhausted her interest in science she began her self-abuse again.

The question might very well be asked : is not such a throwing of self into work a true sublimation, a transference of animal energy into the mental field ? Is it not entirely right to seek satisfaction in mental tasks ? Is not this a genuine overcoming of onanism ?

This can certainly be the case. The mental work then provides life with meaning and fulfilment. It is no longer a substitute but has a value of its own ; it may increase the knowledge or capacity of the subject, raise his standard of life, or serve to help others. In such a connection there can be no question of mental onanism. A genuine satisfaction gained through mental work will overcome the substitute satisfaction gained from self-abuse. Unfortunately, the overcoming is usually not successful. In these cases it is not the kind of action that is decisive but the attitude. If the work is taken up simply as a substitute satisfaction in place of self-abuse, the spiritual dynamic of the individual is not directed towards the true centre of the soul and its fulfilment ; it remains on the periphery of the ego. The egocentric attitude remains unaffected, because it is expressing itself in another form. Therefore, in many cases, the tendency to self-abuse returns as soon as the substitute satisfaction loses its influence.

We have self-abuse in the *religious field*. It is significant that the sexual side of life and the religious should be so near to one another in this connection. For in both cases right fulfilment depends upon the capacity of the individual to get beyond self and become directed towards another personality. This is the law of nature in the field of sex ; and the law of supernature in the religious field.

One form of this religious abuse we find incorporated in the figure of the Pharisee, who builds a wall around himself to protect him against God, and then suns himself in his self-righteousness. If such a man collects good deeds in order to convince himself or others that he is a good man, if he draws attention to his piety or righteousness, as compared with their absence in others, this is certainly a form of spiritual self-abuse. He is abusing a power given to him to enable him to progress beyond self with the aid of Grace, because he seeks to procure self-satisfaction.

One of the commonest forms of spiritual self-abuse is to be found in day-dreaming. This practice can be described in the phrase used sometimes in reference to actual physical self-abuse— " solitary sin." All the symptoms of onanism are seen here, with the exception of the sexual. Such dreaming often occurs as an accompaniment and aid to actual self-abuse. One speaks so glibly of innocent dreams ; and in the world of purely materialistic thought, where only the outward and visible counts, they may assuredly seem innocent, for after all no sin is committed. Many educators would agree with this. But the danger remains that such phantasies may easily serve as an occasion for sin ; thus they should be brought under control

I knew a boy aged fifteen who was mentally lazy, had a poor memory, and no interest in sport. He was full of feelings of inferiority towards his brothers, who did everything " so much better than I can ! " Although his father was a university man, he was sent to a council school, while his brothers, regarded as having better brains, received a superior start in life. Leaving school, he took up a commercial career. He then stole, several times, sums amounting to some thirty pounds. He spent three pounds in buying all sorts of rubbishy sensational books, such as *The Lord of the Wild West* and *The Revenge of the Disinherited*. It was obvious that he identified himself with these heroes of fiction who so easily prevailed over

weaker men—doubtless represented by his brothers. Some eight
pounds was spent in buying an air pistol, a toy revolver, a dagger,
and like equipment.

In such a case, we can say that " innocent " phantasies led to
serious results. But we can go further : is there not an element of
guilt in the phantasies themselves ? When they gain the upper hand
and become an addiction, we are compelled to look upon them as
ethically wrong, even if not exactly morally evil. They must needs
detract from the reality of life and its right fulfilment, a task imposed
upon man by God Himself. Life demands nothing less than our
wholehearted energy, rightly applied to concrete aims, demanding
will power and effort. But what happens in the world of day-
dreams ? The individual occupies himself with an imaginary life in
which he performs imaginary deeds. The forces of the personality are
not turned towards a real goal but towards some fanciful projection.
He leads an unreal life in which the spiritual forces may be absorbed
and exhausted. The analogy to self-abuse is here very obvious.

In the case of these phenomena, as with other forms of the
satisfaction of desire, we must take care not to adopt a strict
" either-or " attitude nor allow it to seem that pleasure or desire is
sinful in *itself*—even with respect to the natural pleasures of married
life. Pleasure is good ; it is a gift of God. St. Thomas Aquinas said
that sexual pleasure in paradise must have been higher and more
perfect than after the Fall. It is a matter of degree, of where the
emphasis is placed. If I seek solely my own pleasure in some action
then it is egocentric and false. It is a matter-of-course that I may
eat to satisfy hunger and that I may rightly enjoy the good things
put before me. But it would not be right were I to eat for the sake
of enjoyment and even, to prolong the enjoyment, cause myself to
be sick, as was frequently done in the ancient world. That is excess.
and gluttony. It is the degree that is decisive. Moderate satisfaction
ensures that the pleasure experienced is not divorced from the
course of nature for egoistic purposes—as it is in self-abuse.

The same argument applies to day-dreams. Excess is the source
of the danger. If, for example, a housewife relaxes in the midst
of monotonous duties, to indulge in phantasies that do not hinder
her actual work, this is assuredly not immoderate or unduly egoistic
conduct ; and she will be ready at once to give her undivided
attention when the nature of the work demands it.

The case of one of my patients presented a very different picture.
The centre of gravity of her life lay in the world of private phantasy:
" I couldn't possibly endure life, were it not for my dream world,"
she said. At the same time, she complained of poor concentration
and difficulties with her work. She could never hold a job for more

than a few weeks, for she was unable to give her whole mind to what she was doing. In the field of sex she was hyper-sensitive and inhibited. For a long time, she had received systematic bladder rinsings from a doctor—clearly as a substitute for self-abuse.

A study of day-dreams readily shows that they serve as substitute satisfactions, much after the manner of self-abuse itself. Those whose lives fall short of their anticipations or who are unsatisfied because they cannot throw themselves into real life, will be very apt to seek unreal satisfaction in some dream world ; they are always open to the danger of losing themselves more and more in phantasies thus squandering their energies. They isolate themselves from real life and its happenings, and become increasingly self-enclosed—a process similar to that noted in the case of those practising self-abuse.

Many people are well aware of the futility of their day-dreaming. Thus a patient of mine was able to recognise the emergence of his dream world as a symptom of an attitude which he knew to be wrong in other fields of life. Much the same may be said about self-abuse, the appearance of which may be regarded as a *signal* that the subject in question has not directed his powers towards an adequate fulfilment of his life, and has remained too absorbed in himself. By way of explaining his mistaken attitude this patient said : " My youthful habit of self-abuse was overcome *de jure*, but not *de facto*." His new knowledge helped him to understand difficulties in his married life.

To sum up, it may be said that we can observe in the mental and spiritual field various forms of what is, in essence, self-abuse—a desire for pleasure turned inwards and divorced from its purpose in nature. The psychic symptoms of such substitute satisfactions are often found in conjunction with the sexual symptoms of self-abuse. The roots of both lie in a false attitude of mind. Thus the forms are often found to be interchangeable.

When the concept of onanism (self-abuse) is thus extended, it becomes obvious that the decisive thing is not the action, which is a *symptom*, but the attitude of mind behind it ; not what is done, but the mental state of the doer. Consider, for example, what is written in John 6 : 28–29—and especially the passage : " This is the work of God that ye believe on him whom he hath sent."

Above action stands *faith* ; the spirit is decisive. It is a wrong attitude of mind that leads to the habit of self-abuse.

Disguised Self-Abuse

In the physical field, too, we know many symptoms which come to light as substitutes for self-abuse within the pattern above described. It is well-known that young children who have been forbidden to play with their sexual parts frequently stop doing this, but very soon take up some other habit : for example, some " nervous symptom," like nail-biting, thumb-sucking, nose-picking, bed-wetting ; in fact almost any of the activities known as " naughtinesses." All these symptoms are interchangeable with one another, and with infantile onanism.

We speak of disguised or latent self-abuse not only in regard to such cases, but in many other relations which may seem quite innocent to the uninitiated. These are often characteristics of self-abuse, suppressed but not overcome. Psychoanalysts will perceive a relation to self-abuse in, for example, such habits as playing with finger rings or purses, poking about with the nose, ears, or lips, picking at fabrics, certain movements with the hands, and a host of other little habits of daily occurrence, suggesting nothing to the lay mind. These phenomena are so common that it is not surprising that a storm of indignation broke out when Freud, for the first time, indicated these connections. W. Steckel rightly calls these disguised forms of onanism ; *negative preoccupations* with the sexual, comparable to what is so often found behind prudishness, the cult of moral indignation, or anxiety about and rejection of sex. Kronfeld and others place all these psychologically related little habits together as modes by which unconscious sexuality seeks to find a solitary path for its gratification. On the other hand A. Gügler rejects this view, while admitting the psychological relation ; but he insists, not without a certain justice, upon a clarity of concept. However, in this study I am concerned with the psychological background and I thus prefer to hold fast to the former viewpoint. For this is the only way in which different actions can be related to the same basic mentality, thereby enabling us to lay the chief weight of our treatment upon the really essential factors : the attitude of mind and the reform of character.

PREVALENCE OF SELF-ABUSE

ALL SIN tends towards isolation, and psychic disorder has the same effect : loneliness is one of the commonest characteristics of neurosis. The victim of self-abuse suffers with special severity from his isolation. This is a part of the very nature of the habit—sometimes referred to as " the solitary sin."

Many of those who practice self-abuse (onanists) believe themselves to be branded by their habit, outcasts from human society. They examine their faces anxiously in the mirror to see if they show the wrinkles underneath the eyes mentioned in the old-fashioned literature warning the young against the habit—wrinkles which may actually be caused by anxiety and fear, and are often entirely lacking in cases where onanism has been practised for years. It very seldom occurs to an onanist that other people, perhaps his immediate neighbours, may have struggled—or may be still struggling—with the same trouble, and it is often a considerable help to him to hear of its great frequency. This hint will be found useful in treating sufferers from the habit ; for it may help to build a bridge, if only a small and fragile one, leading from the isolated victim back to social life.

Thus it may be well at this juncture to quote a few figures, compiled by Rohleder, whose own estimates of the frequency of onanism varied between 85 per cent and 96 per cent.

A Russian questionnaire computes it as 69 per cent. Meirowsky, by questioning students, arrived at the figure of 71 per cent, and, on doctors' evidence, at a higher figure, 88 per cent. Marro examined the material afforded by 450 adult criminals and got 85 per cent. Markuse gave as his opinion that 93 per cent practice the habit, and Dr. Deutsch in Budapest found 96 per cent. Prof. Duck gives the figure of 91 per cent (of whom one third had the opportunity of normal intercourse). Dr. Dukes, a school doctor in England, gave 90 to 95 per cent amongst boys at school. Dr. Scarley of Springfield, Mass., investigated 125 students and gave a figure of 95 per cent, while Brockman found amongst students of theology in the U.S.A., as high a percentage as 99. The figures given by Hirschfeld and Hahn are 96 per cent. Finally Prof. Joung, an American specialist, gave 100 per cent, the same as that found by Prof. Berger ; and Moraglia found that amongst prostitutes (180 cases), the figure was also 100 per cent.

Looking at these enormously high figures one has to accept the fact that the onanist is the rule, and the abstainer the exception. Yet, in spite of these statistics, it is in my experience an exaggeration to assert that everybody, male or female, practices, or has practised, onanism. Lowenfeld also protests against the idea that all men practice self-abuse ; and in regard to women, he says this is a grotesque exaggeration. Dr. Speer writes : " The number of women who seek solace in onanism is an unimportant minority. The great mass of women take no interest in this substitute satisfaction." Yet, on the other hand, American statisticians assure us that female onanism is even more common than male. My own experience, supported by the testimony of priests whom I have questioned, tends to show that it is very prevalent, although probably less so than amongst men.

It will be of interest to ask the question : at what ages is the practice most prevalent ? The evidence demonstrates clearly that the period of puberty is the most critical. The French psychologist Mendousse, who specialised in the problems of youth, after reviewing a wide range of material from various countries, states that everywhere and in every class innumerable young people practice self-abuse. It is possible that many go through the critical time unscathed or at least with few lapses, but—he continues—we have to admit that they are somewhat rare exceptions, at least during the early years of puberty.

Many psychologists feel very doubtful when faced with an adolescent who affirms that, during the entire period of his approaching maturity, he never had anything to do with self-abuse. They are inclined to think that this must be a clear case of a neurotic who has thrust down unwelcome recollections. I know of several young people who managed, in view of specially favourable circumstances, outward and inward, to escape the habit altogether during the period of puberty, but made up for it by taking to the habit during their twenties: some of these cases developed the most marked type of onanism. It gives one pause if one notices, in such cases, delayed mental and spiritual maturity.

Prick and Calon, neuropaths of Nijmegen, have published material demonstrating that self-abuse begins, most commonly, between 12 and 15. Harvey's questionnaires (1932) indicated that self-abuse rose from 15 to 75 per cent between 12 and 18. Meirowsky supports these figures, and states that self-abuse is at its strongest between 14 and 15, some 79 per cent being then affected. Magnus Hirschfeld questioned 436 persons, finding the highest figures for the beginning of the habit to be between 12 and 14. Ramsey, (1943) discussed the matter with 291 boys, and found that 19 per cent had begun before the age of 8 ; and at 15, 98 per cent practised it. Jersild (1946) came to the conclusion that 90 per cent of boys and 50 of girls who had attained to maturity had practised self-abuse once or more than once. Peck and Wells estimated (1923) that 78 per cent of the half-grown boys who were questioned admitted the practice from time to time. The most recent figures are found in the thoroughly misleading Kinsey report : of 6,000 men who were questioned 85 per cent practised self-abuse from the beginning of puberty up to 15.

Finally we have to ask the question : how long does self-abuse go on in individual cases? It is clear from the investigations of Meirowsky and Hirschfeld that 14 per cent practise it for a short period only, 21 for one or two years, 30 per cent for three to four years, and 35 for five to ten years :   thus 65 per cent do not continue for more than four years.   Pursuing this statement, Prick and Calon consider that *a natural relationship* exists between the beginning of self-abuse and a certain period in development, namely puberty.

OCCASIONS FOR SELF-ABUSE

A SENSATION of pleasure associated with sex may appear relatively early.   When a child discovers its bodily self and begins to explore every part, than it will certainly, sooner or later, come to examine the sexual parts.   They are closely related to the " interesting " phenomena of urination and excrementation, which makes them all the more likely to arouse childish curiosity.

At first, however, the sexual regions are not susceptible to excitation.   This can follow only when attention is more or less strongly directed towards sex.   Unfortunately, this take place too often as a result of well-meaning efforts to teach the child " purity."   It will then, very likely, think :   what is it that is so *special* about these regions ?   Further explorations will ensue, until perhaps some real sensations are aroused (see our *Difficulties in Sex Education*).   It is much better to maintain an innocent attitude in this matter.

A child may find out at so early an age as between two and five that it possesses a bodily region which can arouse peculiar sensations of pleasure.   These may be occasioned by a variety of causes. " I found out that it gave my little body pleasure when I lay down flat on my stomach on a table," wrote a woman, describing her experiences as a young child of four and five. Another child of five experienced similar sensations when it clung to the leg of a table and squeezed it.   A little girl of five remarked that it gave her a special sensation of pleasure when she pressed her legs together in a certain manner.   Acts of " self-abuse " on the part of small children may become frequent, when they discover that by rubbing or tickling the genital parts they can procure strange sensations of a pleasurable sort.

Self-abuse in early puberty (8-14) or in puberty (11-17) can arise spontaneously, unless it results as a continuation of—or regression to—earlier practices, or is due to action by others.   If we find that the practice continues without serious interruption from early childhood into the period of puberty, it may well be that we have a case of a difficult type, akin to established onanism ; it is no longer a mere phase of the kind that is likely to pass away of itself.

Let us take an example of the spontaneous discovery of self-abuse. A girl is on her way to school ; she feels that she must " go somewhere," but has no opportunity, and she squeezes her legs together very tightly to hold herself in, and finds that she experiences a strong sensation of pleasure, with sexual spasms. She is delighted with this wonderful discovery and keeps on doing the same thing for years until she reaches maturity when the habit passes off. The girl does not realise until several years later what she had then been doing. In the case of boys, it is often an irritation in the genital zone which causes handling ; this may lead to an erection and finally to pollution. The experience of pleasure during involuntary nocturnal pollution, while half asleep, leads frequently to voluntary abuse.

Self-abuse is very often begun as a consequence of bodily symptoms of an *external* kind which draw attention to the sexual organs—with adults as well as children—thus leading to what is sometimes called accidental self-abuse. For example, eczema, prurigo, pruritus, urticaria (nettle fever), intertrigo (worms which travel from the intestine to the genital zone and cause irritation), phimosis, balanitis (glandular discharge akin to, but not, gonorrhea), pressure of urine in the morning leading to erection, irritation of the genital parts in cycling or pole climbing—as well as many other possibilities.

Internal bodily states are also regarded as predisposing factors in certain cases : such as chronic constipation, and even tuberculosis. Rohleder also mentions convalescence after severe illnesses of a feverish type. A loss of sexual inhibition is particularly likely to occur after encephalitis lethargica.

In addition to the foregoing, we have to reckon with various factors of a psychic nature, predisposing to the practice. Tendencies to self-abuse are to be observed in cases of physical and mental overstrain, when the system is not harmoniously adjusted. In the latter case, one might speak of an attempt at compensation, as with so-called " examination self-abuse."

One often gains the impression that the body calls attention to itself through an urge towards self-abuse, when young people seek to devote themselves too exclusively to the mental field, especially to the cult of pure reason ; and when, through such one-sidedness, they lose the proper balance between body and soul. Further, the state of mind and nerves known as neurasthenia conduces to the habit. Under this head we may include hypersensibility and the weakness of mind and will known as psychasthenia. There also are many cases where climate plays a part, e.g., sudden changes of weather, tending to depress the mind.

But these factors, bodily or mental, do not amount to an actual *compulsion*, impelling to self-abuse, or even to downright addiction to onanism. They act, however, in creating a predisposition. The decisive factors in bringing about an established practice of self-abuse are to be looked for in the depths of the soul ; they find their outward expression in states of anxiety, feelings of displeasure, or imaginative notions (Gügler).

CAUSES AND FORMS OF SELF-ABUSE

IF WE want to help those who suffer from self-abuse we must not fail to examine the predisposing factors mentioned in the foregoing sections. They are especially important when—as in the case of the acute stage of the newly begun habit—they occupy first place. We may consider the case of irritation caused by worms. When the continually recurring cause is removed and the child is not plagued by the worms, self-abuse will in some cases cease.

These factors do not, as we have seen, constitute a compulsion, least of all to an established form of the practice, and treatment cannot confine itself to mastering such causes. We must seek to understand, to probe the background of the sufferer, to find out *why* he practices self-abuse. The question of background and purpose may be called the " contents " of the habit ; the nature of these contents, together with the stage of development of the subject, decides the form and determines the best method of tackling the problem along educational lines.

Self-Abuse in Early Childhood

According to the psycho-analytical school, we may distinguish three phases of childish development : the oral, the anal-erotic, and the sexual. This may appear far-fetched to the layman, but it is grounded in a wealth of experience (see our book : *Difficulties in Life*). In the oral phase, the child receives pleasure by way of the mouth : suckling is associated with sensations of pleasure, and it is the mouth and the regions closely related to it that are concerned in such habits as thumb-sucking, dribbling and nail-biting, the retention of which in later years is regarded as " naughty."

This kind of oral pleasure is quite in order *at that stage* ; and, in the same way, we feel that the child has a claim to be loved and that its urge to develop its ego—to receive rather than to give—is not out of place, as it would be at a later age. According to what we have already learned as to the nature of self-abuse, it would seem possible to class this infantile urge to seek pleasure in the self as a form of self-abuse. This early stage is sometimes known as the auto-erotic.

This relationship with self-abuse is underlined by the fact that experience has shown that attempts to suppress these childish habits is apt to lead to the beginning of childish self-abuse.

The opposite is also found : namely that when children are forbidden to practise infantile self-abuse, they often take to one of the other " naughty " practices. But on no account must we forget that these forms of self-abuse, including the quasi-self-abuse of children, do not fall into the category of real misbehaviour or faults of character, and still less into that of sin, for the simple reason that self-love is proper to the infantile stage. Thus Gebsattel maintains that childish practices akin to self-abuse should not be classed as actual self-abuse at all.

Whatever the practice may be called, it is safe to say that we should take little direct notice, lest the child learns thereby to fix his attention upon it, and may be unable to discontinue the practice without outside aid. The best method is to distract attention and keep him happy and occupied in his daily life, by games and not least, by the warm love that goes out to him. (See our *Difficulties in Sex Education*). More especially with boys, every reference to sex, to purity, or to sin, is utterly mistaken at this stage of development : the child simply *does not know what you are talking about*, and what he does not understand is apt to become a burden to him. With girls, one is sometimes compelled to say a few words : signs of inflammation of the genital parts appear, due to rubbing or scratching, and these can lead to a fixation of the mind on the body. A mother who notices such signs (which may be due to other causes, such as strong urine, tickling stockings, or merely a lack of cleanliness) should do no more that say that these parts should be as carefully treated as the nose or eyes—and everyone knows that the eyes must not be rubbed or scratched or they will become inflamed and painful.

Self-Abuse in Childhood

When a child of six or even ten years of age is found to be continuing in the childish practices referred to above, including so-called self-abuse, or when he begins such practices at this time, we have to ask ourselves what is at the bottom of the matter. In my view we can distinguish two basically different types. One is the so-called playful self-abuse : this comes under the heading of curiosity and self-exploration rather than under that of downright shamelessness—although the latter element may play a part at times. This playful type of abuse is far from being a compulsion towards seeking pleasure. Its mainspring is the child's desire to investigate something strange in himself. We should be justified in not reckoning this type of practice as a genuine self-abuse ; the latter is characterised by its near relationship to established onanism and its markedly sexual emphasis. This relatively innocent form will disappear of itself when the child is trained to a true sense of shame and a realisation of the *value* of sex, given the needful help in self-understanding through a prudent degree of enlightenment, and not disturbed by a false type of sex education.

At the same age we may, however, find another form of the habit. This has significance as the expression of a maladjustment to the world and the self. It may begin in consequence of the increased demands that life makes upon the child. Or it may be a continuation of the earlier childish form which should not be more than a passing phase. If, however, this phase persists, it changes its nature; what was formerly a childish practice becomes something less innocent and the child is himself aware of this; feelings of guilt and anxiety tend to appear.

We have seen that for the young child to turn his energies inwards towards the self is a phase of development; but with increasing age they should be directed less towards the self and more towards the outer world. Should this new orientation fail to take place we have to seek the reason for the failure to achieve normal development. We must examine the background of the child's life. As educators, we must ask ourselves : are *we ourselves*, perhaps, to blame? Has the child felt that he was not sufficiently loved, and for this reason has not been able to give love? Or is he perhaps in need of some kind of comforting? In our book, *Difficulties in Life*, we have dealt with educational mistakes in relation to childish feelings of insecurity, anxiety, inferiority and inhibition. As with other faults, childish self-abuse may become an addiction and we have to discover what lies behind it; what is the child looking for that he has recourse to such a substitute? Is it love—is it some help that we should have given?

A child may feel himself to be insufficiently loved for various reasons. It may be true that he is not loved enough; or it may seem so to him because of his place in the family; or because he suffers from some weakness in his nature which demands an extra portion of love. It is very difficult to give the right amount of love; parents and educators are generally either too severe or too lenient. They are very apt to make mistakes which undermine the child's confidence in himself and in the world, so that he suffers from insecurity and anxiety, compensation for which is too often sought through self-abuse. He is disappointed and turns away from the world represented to him, primarily, by his mother. Failing to receive from her the affection and attention he needs, he seeks consolation by giving affection and attention to himself. This he finds in self-abuse, which now takes on the character of a comforter.

This type of practice may carry with it—even before puberty begins—an imaginative inner life of a sexual nature which may be turned to a particular person. The child pictures to himself all sorts of acts of tenderness and sexual embraces, even the act of sexual union itself, according to the extent of the knowledge he has acquired.

He will be all the more likely to picture an unknown and unexplored form of love—that is, the sexual—if the old forms of love between mother and child have failed to satisfy his craving for love. How far it is actually a case of subjective rebellion against purity, I cannot say. Can one speak in this connexion of a subjective guilt ? Is it, perhaps, the child's nature to display irreverence towards the true meaning of sex ? Is it possible, in this framework, to apply the definition of Ruland, that unchastity is the separation of pleasure from duty? In many cases at least this would seem to be out of the question.

In association with the child's subjective feeling that he has not received sufficient love, we may readily find a feeling of being overburdened—whether objectively true or not : the claims of school ; a position as eldest of a number of children ; a need for taking the mother's place ; or perhaps the fact of being a species of buffer to absorb the shock of marriage conflicts or other parental difficulties. These and many other factors may weigh so heavily upon the childish mind that, in default of other possibilities, he seeks compensation in self-abuse. In the world of to-day, inward anxiety, fear of life involving withdrawal into the self, are often due to all sorts of environmental influences damaging to a child : for example, lack of an ordered family life ; unhappy marriage relationships, with their conflicts ; the emptiness of daily life ; and, not least, contact with the immoral or amoral character of the surrounding world. This situation has been touched upon when we considered the problem of the wide gap between spiritual and bodily maturity. There is nothing to surprise us in the fact that self-abuse amongst the young has increased of recent years.

The vague, indefinable anxiety which permeates the atmosphere of the modern world may lie at the bottom of many disturbances, such as sleeplessness. Connected with this is the use of self-abuse as an aid to sleep, practised by not a few adults as well as by children.

If we are successful in tracing the real cause of anxiety in good time and then helping the child to overcome it and to find elsewhere what he is looking for, than the self-abuse will gradually diminish and disappear. This can take place without any mention of the practice. But if a well-established habit with its guilt complex, its vain struggles, and its self-contempt, has been formed, the child is in urgent need of help. The habit will by then have taken on the character of firmly rooted onanism, a most difficult problem for both educator and priest. In both types it is a most dubious policy to make an open attack upon the habit, by using negative means in an attempt to end it. Our efforts must be directed towards enticing the child away from his ego fixation, by introducing him to aims and interests which take him away from self. Our support, our confidence, our manifest belief in his value, will give him courage to venture beyond self. Restrictions and warnings coming from the educator are likely to promote a fixation of instinctive urges upon the self.

Self-Abuse in Early Puberty

At first the child is completely enmeshed in his world of phantasy and only very gradually does he find his way towards reality. The day-dreams of his little world of play and fairy tales form a preliminary stage in his progress towards reality, a species of " trying out " of the life he is about to enter. This stage is comparable to a bud not yet open, but carrying within itself the form of the flower. The child realises dimly that he is budding, and he dreams of the future flowering.

Pre-puberty is marked by an increasing tendency to turn towards the outside world ; and this is followed by a return to a new interest in self which characterises early puberty. It is just as if a time of collecting and storing up power was needed, before taking the great plunge into puberty itself. The young boy or girl listens to an inner voice and feels the call to advance into real life. He realises dimly the possibilities that lie within, ready to blossom. The inwardness of this phase has been rightly called by Gügler an introversion required by the phase of growth. This is to say that the turning of dynamic force inwards towards the discovery of self in a deeper way is not a fault at this time, but a phenomenon proper to the period, just as the same thing was in early infancy. Introversion, combined with the emerging of the not yet comprehensible urges of sex, both so prominent at this stage, are obviously factors making for the practice of self-abuse. If, at the same time, one of the external factors to which we have referred should make itself felt—for example if the young person is taught bad habits by another—then the adolescent will become a victim of self-abuse for a longer or shorter time.

If the habit were of such a nature that we could regard it as a phase, as in early infancy, there would be no question of " sin " in an objective sense. But we have to deal with another factor : the emergence of sex in a fuller sense. This may be met in two *wrong* ways : firstly, it may be dealt with on the surface by a surrender to self-abuse, which is of course no solution whatever ; secondly, it may be approached prematurely. The first may be regarded as a flight from reality, a thrusting of sex to the periphery of life. (See our volume on sex education). If the adolescent fails to develop the spiritual forces needed for his sex problem, and if he does not receive effective aid from parents or educators, he is likely to continue his exploration of the urge within him and to become more and more enmeshed in the habit of self-abuse, and finally to become a confirmed onanist. The second possibility is that the adolescent will try to anticipate sex in the fullest sense. This is more likely if his imagination is filled with sexual images. The healthy-minded boy, on the other hand, will be able to keep himself from premature experiments, if he is aided from within and without. If, in the days of early puberty, when the mind ought to be concerned with the development of personality and the awakening of the capacity for pure love, the element of bodily sexuality takes first place, this constitutes an anticipation of a stage proper to a more mature age and is damaging to the individual.

There is a positive significance in the preoccupation with sex in these early years, since it forms a preparation for the time when its real values can be perceived. This meaning cannot include the idea of a partner in love. The " other " cannot even be envisaged, for the adolescent is not far enough advanced in the development of his own individuality ; thus, without the materialisation of a real partner, he remains in the preliminary stages of love life. The self-abuse of these years forms a possible—although not inevitable—preliminary phase in the practical direction of the adolescent towards a real union. It involves a species of imaginary, dream-like, tentative approach to the future time, when life and love are centred on the WE and not the I.

It is often stated that self-abuse in early puberty is not wrong or pathological, but perfectly normal and right, and this view finds support in experiences not to be too lightly dismissed. It can be pointed out that the vast majority of young people have indulged in self-abuse at one time or another, and that it is hardly to be credited that grave sin is the normal approach to life, or that it can be so damaging as is often supposed. Nor should we overlook another point : many adolescents, if they have not been subjected to well-meaning talks about the sinfulness of the habit, practise it, at this stage, without any feeling of guilt. Yet, at another stage, this feeling may arise quite spontaneously. We shall take up the problem of guilt in a later section.

Young people get over the self-abuse of early puberty quickly, given the right kind of help to overcome their introspective phase and turn their minds outwards again. What we have said about the understanding of self-education in the value of purity, social life,

and the right aims for youthful sexuality, finds its application here.
The typical self-abuse of this period is not to be taken unequivocally
as a sign of spiritual or sexual trouble ; but it is an indication that
some help may be needed and that the teacher should give careful
guidance. He will avoid breeding anxiety and guilt complexes by
talk about " vice " or " depravity." This will be discouraging and
will lead all too easily to a real fixation in a confirmed type of
onanism.

It is well to be as innocent as possible when faced with the habit,
however much one may feel grieved to see that the boy (or girl)—
usually through some environmental fault—has drifted into it.
One will endeavour to turn the attention of the boy and one's own
attention also, towards mental and spiritual opportunities. On no
account must the right kind of enlightenment be overlooked ; it
should be handled thoroughly and in such a manner as to arouse
feeling for the value and sacredness of sex itself—for this is the
foundation of purity.

Onanism as a Symptom

Many of those who suffer deeply on account of an established
habit of self-abuse trace their downfall, above all, to a lack of the
right sort of enlightenment. Thus :

" I am grateful to my dear parents for more than I can tell.
But in one thing they failed me : before the time of puberty they
should have explained to me many things I did not then understand.
I had no one to help me and was not able by myself to master the
problem of sex. I feel filled with shame when I think of how I fell
into sin. The sensation of guilt, the fact of falling again and again,
the continuance of this habit into the years of manhood, depressed
me heavily. In fact my whole life is so overshadowed that I can
never again feel really joyful and happy."

The feeling of guilt is regarded by many writers on this problem
as itself the cause of self-abuse : but I look upon this view as
one-sided. The feeling of guilt gnaws at the mind, eating away the
energies of life and undermining faith in the future. The victim is
so hemmed in by self-reproach that he loses the capacity to look at
his life objectively, and fails to perceive other and far more important elements. He becomes blind to the world of values and to
his own failings in other directions : in love or in the tasks of every
day.

" I never got an answer to my questions from my parents. When,
at the age of five, I began to practise sexual play I had the feeling
that it was not right. But when I was old enough to go to confession
I persuaded myself that it could not be a serious sin, and did not

mention it. However, a continual sense of sin plagued me. For years I thought that I was not worthy to receive the Sacraments, but I never found the courage to come out with my trouble. The feeling of guilt drove me to self-abuse, which I still practise, although I fight against it all the time. If I had received proper enlightenment, everything would have been much easier.

Let us consider what all this involves : a whole life under mental distress ; a youth full of anxiety ; no confidence in parents or priest ; deep depression and discouragement lasting for many years . . . and we must remember that this not an exceptional case. What a sad history of loneliness, obstinacy, lack of love and of a helping hand, depression and self-reproach this represents, not to mention the endlessly fruitless struggle to abandon the habit.

One must realise that onanism is never conquered by the method of direct attack. Such a method centres the mind on the habit, so that it tends to get worse. The cause itself must be sought out and removed : it is therefore of primary importance to discover the deeper roots of the trouble.

When does the habit make its appearance ? More especially at times of depression and dissatisfaction ; after disappointments and reverses ; after differences with the environment or other discouraging experiences ; at times of monotony and inner emptiness and loneliness. An unsatisfied yearning for love may give rise, according to the character of the subject and those around him, either to self-abuse through yearning, or self-abuse as a species of revenge. We notice that the habit diminishes or vanishes when such circumstances as the above are changed. We frequently hear it said : " Since I found someone whom I can love, the habit has ceased," or, " During a time when I was filled with enthusiasm for something, I was not troubled with it." In the course of a cycling tour lasting for some days and giving him many new and beautiful impressions, an established onanist reported that he was free from the habit ; and it can happen that during the military service period, when the subject is occupied from morning to night with this or that duty, onanistic addicts find themselves relatively free. These examples may be multiplied many times.

Onanism is very frequently found as a symptom of *opposition* to the surrounding world. It has been described by Hermann Maas in his book, *An klaren Wassern*, as the " Revolt of the Weaklings." The strong adolescent is quite open in his oppositional phase of puberty. He rebels very sharply against authority and the word " don't." The weak character carries out his opposition in secret by means of " oppositional self-abuse ; " while, at the same time, gloating over his cleverness in doing something forbidden, in getting the better of his parents and teachers. In married life, self-abuse can have an oppositional character as a revolt against a tie which an oppositional type (possibly subconsciously) may find too irksome. Many of those who have taken to marriage as a means of overcoming their self-abuse—that is, for egoistic reasons—but who are not able to shoulder all the consequences of a union with another, continue the habit to a greatly increased extent after marriage and, if they cannot manage otherwise, they enlist the aid of sexual stimulants. It is as if they wanted to say : " I can manage for myself—you are not needed." This situation can arise also with women.

A disturbed relationship to the surrounding world can have a twofold origin. We find factors indigenous to the natural period of revolt associated with puberty. They need not be taken too seriously for they tend to pass off ; it need not be assumed that they will lead to an established habit of self-abuse. But we find, also, others of a graver nature which have deeper roots : they derive from the parent and usually have a long history of isolation in conjunction with neurosis.

We are now in possession of a number of factors which give us pause : unsatisfied yearning for love, due either to a lack of love or to pampering love ; a disturbed domestic background, itself often a sign of unsuccessful love in the home ; discouragement, increased by the failure to impart to the child a positive outlook and sufficient self-confidence ; inadequate enlightenment or an authoritarian attitude, for which parents or teachers are to blame ; inward emptiness, again indicating faults on the part of the educators, who have not understood how to provide the child with a firm basis and a knowledge of the meaning and purpose of life ; anxiety ; insecurity ; depression ; isolation ; and, finally, loneliness, the root symptom of onanism. Looking closely at these factors, we must be struck by the fact that they are the same as those found in the history of neurosis. We are thus faced with the question : *Is onanism a neurosis* ? Let us look at other conditions with the same history : an ulcerated stomach ; nervous heart trouble ; asthma ; obsessional actions ; or depressions. Onanism is another symptom of the same kind. H. von Hattingberg calls it the most prevalent of all the monosymptomatic neuroses ; at any rate it is one of the possible reactions of the neurotic character. We can now say that onanism is a symptom of the individual who cannot deal adequately with himself, and with life and the world in general ; he is in a state of psychic disorder. Gügler states that long established self-abuse is nearly always a symptom revealing abnormal reactions in feeling and character. The degree of onanism is directly related to the degree of neurosis.

Sexual trouble is always part of a larger trouble, of a difficulty in tackling life. It is characteristic of the man who cannot deal with himself or others. Like all neurotic symptoms, onanism has its roots in the subconscious. It tells us that something is seriously wrong in our relationship to ourselves, to the community, and to life ; and, above and beyond these things, to God himself. It is a *danger signal* that we should do well to heed. You cannot go on like that, it seems to say. You must change your way of life—you must *develop*.

In the background of onanism we perceive all the factors making for neurosis. These make themselves felt in the field of sex, for this is also the field of organic social life ; this is in keeping with the character of neurosis, which is always more or less connected with social disorder and loss of contact. It is an expression of an inner division, indicating a failure to adopt a positive attitude towards bodily life and a refusal to accept the reality of the element of personal evil in the depths of the soul. Thus, onanism appears more especially in connection with other neurotic symptoms and—as we should indeed expect—at the time of puberty when the individual is called upon to adjust himself to social life, and growth towards maturity. The typical accompanying characteristics of this period (already described in some detail) are calculated to produce the symptom of onanism.

Thus we may attribute to onanism a special function: it forces us to pay attention to that part of our being which we do not want to notice—the forces of the subconscious. But this very unwillingness conceals a tendency towards these very forces—the despised hidden urges of sex. Desires that were buried and disguised break out : for example, I may have an Oedipus complex which I have not the knowledge or courage to face. I will not admit to a mother fixation (in the case of the male) and, instead of freeing myself from this tie, I turn inwards and seek a sexual outlet in myself, since the moral censor makes the idea of union with my mother impossible. In this way I manage to avoid facing the situation and overcoming it.

Onanism is always the same thing. It is a substitute for love—born in loneliness and causing increased loneliness : a vicious circle. The best way of breaking out of this circle is to experience and learn genuine love. This love has many forms : the love of self in its true form, demanding self-perfection ; the love of a partner ; love for a human social group ; and, finally, the love of God.

One cannot help being surprised that a true recognition of onanism as a symptom, and not a vice or a disease, is so rarely found, particularly in the care of souls. Yet this view is by no means new. And it is of decisive importance in giving aid to those who suffer from this trouble. Surely we have long ago passed beyond the time when medicine looked upon onanism as a disease of a special kind, and attempted to treat it by the most unlikely means. (See the chapter on Treatment later in this study).

Onanism by Necessity

We have not, so far, taken up the problem of a type of onanism that is one of the most prevalent, at least amongst adults : onanism practised under the pressure of circumstances. The reader should be warned, however, that there are no clear-cut distinctions such as onanism by necessity, or ordinary onanism. In self-abuse there are no such sharp lines. But it is worth while to explain the characteristics of each type, as long as we remember that one form can merge with another, and one form can develop into another.

In treating of typical onanism, we pointed out that it is not always cured by marriage, but can persist after union of the normal type is possible. This is decidedly not the case with onanism of the " necessary " type. We have, therefore, to make a distinction between the neurotic anti-social type, rooted in the subconscious, and the type of onanism likely to be practised by those who find themselves forced into isolation by some outward circumstances.

In the case of ordinary onanism, the phantasies which accompany it are of a solitary nature ; another person may be imagined but merely as an aid to the practice—not as a real entity. The whole proceeding is egocentric. But, with onanism caused through outward pressure, the imaginary world of the subject is directed towards a definite loved partner. The sexuality of the subject would find its outlet along normal lines were it not for the pressure exerted by obstacles of a moral, sociological, spatial, or other order. According to Oswald Schwarz, the hetero-erotic onanism of young people may be regarded as a transitional form leading to the normal outlet.

The social structure of to-day is a main factor in this " necessary " type of onanism. In the case of races living on a natural level, young people marry on reaching maturity, while with us there is usually a long interval of, say, 10 or 15 years. Some look for a solution in pre-marital intercourse ; others in self-abuse. Many do both : few do neither.

It is a matter of experience that it is the better types, morally, who refuse to take the first course : they say, not without justice, that in the pre-marital relationship one is not only sinning one self but leading a person one loves into sin at the same time—which is much worse. In their view, self-abuse is the lesser of the two evils. In the same category we may place those whose partner is dead or who are separated for some reason from husband or wife. Under normal circumstances none of those would think of practising self-abuse.

The distinction is therefore essential : on the one hand, we have a type of onanism caused by *unconscious* factors in a neurotic character ;   on the other, a practice conditioned by *consciously* realised external factors. Is the subject inwardly unfitted for normal life, or is he the victim of outward causes ?

Yet it is obvious that no sharp line can be drawn. In my view, it is often just a question of emphasis upon this or that factor, tipping the scale one way or the other. Through the coming of a real love, onanism can disappear—passing, possibly, through an intervening stage of onanism by necessity.

Fairly often we are able to distinguish a third stage with ill-defined boundaries. In this, the world of the imagination is taken up with a vague or transitory partner, and yet it is more than a yearning for love ; there is a definite *readiness* for a real tie with a person not as yet clearly seen, but anticipated. Gebsattel draws our attention to a factor of a constitutional nature which is often found in cases of onanism from necessity. This is the co-called " sexual constitution," in which the urge towards ejaculation of the semen is exceptionally vehement and imperative. We have two factors operating together. In the first place, the desired union with the partner cannot or must not take place ; in the second, the urge of instinct is too powerful to be withstood. It is logical that this type of onanism should become superfluous as a result of marriage.

Gebsattel's thesis is of special importance, because it counters the view often put forward in pedagogical and clerical quarter to the effect that this problem is one of *will power*. A stronger will would prevail. But, according to Gebsattel's theory, it is not weakness of character or anything pathological that is the decisive factor, but the strength of the sexual constitution.

Related to both sexual constitution and onanism by necessity is a phenomenon which causes trouble to the consciences of many young men : a lover tenderly embraces his fiance, and this results in an ejaculation of semen, and he asks himself whether this is a form of self-abuse. According to what we have already learned about self-abuse, this phenomenon is radically different. It is not a solitary act, but takes place in warm relation to the object of love ; it is a species of reaction following involuntarily upon a normal loving action. It does not come under the head of mutual self-abuse; for the man is not seeking sensual pleasure for himself, but making an advance motivated by real love.

CONSEQUENCES OF ONANISM

IN EARLIER times it was customary to threaten the most dire consequences as a means of frightening young people away from onanism. No other means of dealing with it was known. The causes, accompanying phenomena, and results of the habit were all mixed up together ; for there was then no real knowledge of the habit. The whole matter was, in fact, in a state of confusion.

The following were quite erroneously regarded as consequences : diseases of the brain and spinal column ; mental and physical weakness ; degeneration to the point of collapse ; hysteria ; hypochondria ; profound emotional disturbances ; impotence ; female sterility ; manic-depressive psychosis ; dementia praecox ; progressive paralysis ; epilepsy and consumption. One can imagine how tortured many onanists were by these fearful pictures of their possible future. It is true that many, out of sheer terror, may really have ceased the practice. But they did not *overcome* it, and the mental state of which the practice was a symptom remained the same.

More serious than these pictures were the consequences that followed upon the terroristic method. The subjects were, in many cases, young people of a highly sensitive and easily swayed type. If, for example, an onanist is told that he will become impotent, this alone may be enough to render him so, from psychogenic causes. If he hears that headaches will follow, it will not be long before he gets a headache.

Speer states that the glands producing semen cannot give more than they produce. If there is no more, the desire to practice abuse ceases automatically. Nobody has ever been ruined by self-abuse. Occasional excesses cause no more damage than occasional excesses of any other sort, while continual excesses are not possible. Speaking of female onanism, Speer regards inflammation of the membrane of the genitals as the only possible bad result. No organic damage can be done.

Gügler, following upon a detailed examination of the subject, says that onanism, as such, has no evil consequences for bodily health ; there is no disease and no damage which can be traced to the habit as its specific cause.

However, various writers consider nervous conditions of the heart and nervous gastric trouble as deriving from this habit, in certain cases (Posner, Hirschfeld, von Gruber, Kafemann, Löwenfeld, Ziehen). In my own view, a symptom of one disease is here made responsible for another. On this point, Gügler says that in the majority of cases, an exact examination will always show that chronic or excessive onanism is a consequence of, or accompanies some already existent disorder, so that we have no right to hold the onanism responsible for particular symptoms—even indirectly.

In the case of female self-abuse, a possible consequence must be considered. If the masturbation is practised entirely with the clitoris, it is possible that a fixation of the pleasurable excitation upon this part may result (*clitorismus*). Women who suffer from this become incapable of experiencing pleasure in the vagina or womb in married relations, and are deprived of their full satisfaction. It should be remarked, however, that *clitorismus* can result from other causes, such as hypersensibility or immaturity of the reflexes.

Any other consequences which may be brought forward may be regarded, at the most, as *indirect* consequences : in the physical field as a predisposition to or mental intensification of some disordered state. The Cahiers Laënnec* mentions disturbances in the urinary passages, weakening of muscular tone, lumbar pains, anorexia, and disturbances of sleep.

The consequences depend in part upon the frequency of the practice : they are more probable if it begins early and is practised to excess, and if the educational attitude of the educators is devoid of understanding. This is especially the case for the *psychic* consequences such as feelings of anxiety or guilt, self-reproaches, and fears regarding mental and bodily health (sexual neurasthenia). Apart from such consequences, there is nothing which can justly be attributed to onanism. Even this statement requires some modification, since anxiety and feelings of guilt can arise in the case of any neurosis.

THE MORAL PROBLEM

A young man who had been given to self-abuse for many years and suffered from a strong sense of guilt, determined to clear up the question of how gravely his sin should be regarded. Sometimes he went to confession twice a day, so that he had a good opportunity of finding out how widely divergent were the views taken by different spiritual directors. On the one extreme he was told that his practice was not a sin at all but an illness ; on the other, he was threatened with the direst penalties for a sin that cried to Heaven. Others, occupying a middle position, told him that his sin was not mortal, but one of the more serious venial sins which he might well confess before receiving Communion.

Another young man told me of a saying that he had heard during a mission : " The worst sin is that which attacks the forces of life." He had been quite shattered by these words. The moral theologian Schilling regards self-abuse as akin to murder, while

* See *New Problems in Medical Ethics, Series I* (Mercier Press).

André Snoeck, S.J., of Louvain said, in *New Problems in Medical Ethics*, Series I : "Christian morality has always held as an evident truth that self-abuse is a grave sin. That is both the common senti-ment of fervent Christianity and the common and certain doctrine sustained with vigour by the moralists. There is no probability therefore that the Church will ever permit anyone to teach that masturbation could constitute a light fault. Such laxity is quite unthinkable. Compromises in the field of interior chastity produce in the individual a revulsion against holiness and against all that is divine in human life."*

Although we agree with P. Snoeck that the habit is, objectively considered, a grave sin, we have to bear in mind that we cannot rightly speak of the habit as a mortal sin, subjectively at least, in very many cases. There are three conditions attaching to a mortal sin : gravity of the matter itself, clarity of knowledge, and free choice. All three are very seldom involved in the habit we are considering.

To obtain a precise view of the problem, we must go back to the fundamental principle that sin is a spiritual act. A turning away from God (*aversio Dei*) can be performed only in the spirit. An act cannot be regarded as a unity, except by considering the purpose underlying it. It is the business of psychology to discover such purposes. It is therefore neither unnecessary not irrelevant for the doctor and the psychologist to take a hand in clarifying the problem of self-abuse and sin.

Impurity and Sin

It is frequently brought up against Catholics that their religion pivots about the sixth commandment, which bears the chief em-phasis in the practical care of souls ; and that, in comparison, the gospel of joy and the commandment of love play a very minor part. It will be useful to examine this question and see what motives lie behind the charge. It is possible that in this way something will emerge that will be valuable in our treatment of the moral problem of self-abuse.

With this end in view, it will be illuminating, in my opinion, to make an excursion into the field of mythology. In the case of prim-itive peoples, and also with the Greeks and Romans, we find a significant religious practice. To reduce this to its simplest terms, it was felt that the blood of the menstruating or child-bearing woman, as well as the seed of the man, are impure or are a *cause* of impurity ; they stain men and women and make them unfit to draw near to the gods, for they attract evil spirits.

*See "Masturbation and Grave Sin," p.35.

It is not a matter of guilt or moral stain ; the act of intercourse itself was not regarded as morally impure in itself, but as causing unfitness in a religious and ceremonial sense. One again became pure through ceremonial washings. Those who sought to approach the gods without such washing were guilty of a grave act of sacrilege. Amongst the Jews we find similar customs. The emission of semen and the flow of blood make men and women impure until the sun goes down (Lev. 15 : 16–18) ; they are unworthy to come near to holy things (I Kings 21) or to serve in a holy war.

Through the early Middle Ages down to the sixteenth century— indeed sometimes down to the present day—we encounter similar modes of thought without conscious relationship to historical myths. In my own practice, I have come across several women who said that, even as girls, they never went to Communion during the menstruation periods. They had a feeling that they were impure— but not a feeling of sin. They did so entirely as a result of their own instinct and without any direction from outside.

We may well ask what sort of factors were here at work ? What are we to understand by blood and semen attracting evil spirits ? Is this some ancient superstition, some forgotten myth or perhaps a primeval instinct ? We do not know. But I would venture the suggestion that it is the *autonomy* of the unconscious that is at the root of the matter: the demonic character of those obscure and powerful forces, not subject to control by the conscious will and dwelling in the depths of personality. The demonic force of the complex of unconscious life-forces may be thought of as making men and women unclean in a religious sense ; for in sexuality these forces can take command over the conscious *ego*—at least for a time. The individual then becomes the prey of the earthy elements and is no longer free to raise his spirit towards God.

This impurity in a religious sense does not accordingly signify evil or sin, but the admixture of the spirit with the forces of the *id*. The washing represents the liberation and refreshment of the spiritual self and the restoration of unity of personality. The time factor (until the setting of the sun, or " two days away from a woman ") creates the distance felt to be needful for the *ego* to free itself and regain purity.

The demonic element represents not only the instinctive sexual factor, but also the element of *personal evil* lying in wait in the depths of the soul. Man is afraid of both, since he feels they are hostile to his personality. Primitive fear of demonic evil and of the autonomous demonic sex element unite to produce a single primeval fear ; and it is often impossible for the conscious mind to distinguish between the two factors.

There arises, accordingly, a state of mind in which the sex element is stamped with the mark of primeval evil, and is looked upon as doubly sinful. Thus we get Manicheanism and allied trends of thought : evil is identified with the body. The organs of sex are made to represent all that is evil and unclean. There follows the overemphasis (still with us) of the sixth commandment as the law for preserving purity. In this way ceremonial, religious purity, in the sense explained above, is not distinguished from moral purity ; on the contrary, through being stamped as a sin of impurity, it is doubly underlined.

Have we not asked ourselves again and again why this unfortunate overemphasis upon sex, with its negative fixation, should so burden the whole of our Christianity, despite the sane and balanced teachings of her great theologians as well as the Christian revelation ? Why should a contemporary like August Adam have to declare that it was *a religion of love* that Christ preached ? (Adam, *Der Primat der Liebe*, 1939). Why should it still be the case, in the care of souls, that sins of commission are so often taken more seriously than sins of omission ? It seems to me that we are still drawing heavily upon the legacy of old Jewish and pagan conceptions. The notion of " double impurity," explained above, makes it clear enough why sins against the sixth commandment seem to count more heavily than all the others. This is all the more painful when we remember that this whole attitude rests upon misunderstanding and indeed, in part, upon ancient mythology and not upon the Christian revelation !

The picture, however, is not altogether discouraging. Of late we note a withdrawal from the old view of the sixth commandment as dominating the moral field, a development rendered necessary by our increasing knowledge of human nature, psychological histories, and the autonomous character of the unconscious. This knowledge robs the unconscious of its demonic character, in proportion as we discover more about instinctive forces and the element of personal evil dwelling in the depths of the soul.

Objective Guilt

The following section does not constitute an attempt by a layman to lay down the law in moral and theological matters, where he has no competence. It is a psychological and ontological investigation of the nature of wrong conceptions and attitudes. Thus we ask : Apart from all personal and unconscious motives, in what does the sin of self-abuse actually consist ?

Does it consist in the " forbidden lust of the flesh " ? A consideration of the foregoing passages will make it clear that we should perhaps be more careful in defining our concept of forbidden carnal pleasure, because experience shows that it does not go deep enough to reach the root of the matter. The late Middle Ages, however, arrived at a doctrine which still possesses validity.

According to this teaching, sexual pleasure was forbidden if it were sought after voluntarily, as the prime motive (*in se volita se directe quaesita*) of an act, which by virtue of its nature, should have something other and higher as its central meaning : thus, in married intercourse, this meaning is the building up of the family, mutual fulfilment through love, and the bringing into existence of new life.

Seen from this angle, the pleasure attached to self-abuse must be wrong in itself, for it seeks through an organ, the meaning of which is other and higher, a pleasure centred in self and divorced from the above aims. This argument, based upon the essence of sex itself, seems at first sight convincing and adequate.

Yet we have to ask the question : is it really pleasure, the *delectatio venerea*, which makes self-abuse sinful ? Or is it possible that the above view needs to be examined more closely ? We feel the wrongness of the action and seek to pin down the essential element of sin. Those which leap to the eye are : first, the pleasure ; and secondly, the squandering of the semen, the life-giving element. To both of these the responsibility has been attributed.

But we have to remember that many people given to self-abuse do not practice it on account of the pleasure, but, for example, in order to get rid of an unbearable feeling of tension. " I feel so restless that I am unfit for any sort of mental work ; and I know that when this is relieved I can work again ". Such a remark is often heard from an onanist. The notion that the habit is a pursuit of pleasure falls to the ground in considering these cases ; to many of them the act itself is intensibly disagreeable. Angermaier regards the pleasure theory as untenable and explains that the chief reason for the practice cannot lie in the quest for forbidden pleasure.

What is the position with respect to the squandering of the semen ? Jewish tradition teaches that the sinfulness of onanism lies in the wasting of the life-giving element. It may here be remarked that this argument would not apply to the practice, if carried out by women, men over the age of procreation, or children ; but apart from this, the argument does not hold. All through nature we find that the seeds of life are squandered on a colossal scale. Every ejection releases some 100,000,000 seeds. In the case of a reputedly large family of twelve children, only a dozen life-carrying cells actually perform their assigned task, while thousands of millions are wasted by nature.

Where then are we to look for the sin ? We have examined various forms of self-abuse and found that we cannot place them on the same level. We ask again in reference to the sinfulness : what is there *in common* between the various forms which can bring them all under the head of sin ?

This common factor is, in my view, the fact that self-abuse contradicts the *essential meaning of sex* and the inner reality of the organs themselves and is thus a perversion of the true order. The act of sex should be an expression of love between two human beings, the union of heart and mind expressed as carnal union—an order reversed in onanism, when the organs are employed in a manner divorced from their true function. This is the deepest sense in which the practice is sinful. It is a breach of the divine order of nature—the natural law.

Here another question may be put : Is this natural law to be found in the Decalogue ; and if so, where ? Against what commandment does self-abuse sin ? Many theologians have held the view that the sin is against the fifth, which forbids the taking of life. No doubt they have in mind the " murder " of the squandered life-giving seed. But in this case every husband, even when he begets a child, is a million times a murderer. A seed cell cannot be looked upon as half a human being. It is possible that some part is played by the alleged bad consequences to health of the practice ; but we know that this theory, too, is not acceptable. In my own opinion we cannot do better than stick to the old sixth commandment: after saying, " Thou shalt not commit adultery," we find in the old Jewish law also the corollary " or do any unclean thing." Wherein consists this unclean thing ? This is clear from the above. It consists in the misuse of the organs intended for love. Beyond the sixth commandment, the basic law of love, upon which the whole law rests, is even more deeply violated. The turning away of the spirit from love is most clearly manifested through the organs of sex, for they are more intimately related to love than any other parts.

We must not overlook another important reason for the objective sinfulness of self-abuse. We have already spoken of the divorce of the animal part of the soul, so closely associated with the body, from the spiritual part, associated with the mind. This division is increased by neurosis, with its breakdown of communication between body and soul, and between the conscious soul and the subconscious. Objectively considered, this is a wrong state of things — an act of *aversio,* a turning away from the harmony and self-discovery demanded by the divine order.

Yet another psychological point should be mentioned : the anthropological pattern of the human being indicates a struggle to rise beyond himself and turn towards others, towards the world, and ultimately towards God Himself. Therefore, the egocentric fixation of the onanist may rightly be looked upon as a kind of *regression*, as a spiritual *aversio*, an evasion of the divine purpose which is the development and fulfilment of life. Furthermore, the task of humanity demands an ascent from the animal towards the mental and spiritual level, called to leadership over the lower levels. When the natural sexual urge acquires domination over the demands of the spirit, we find a disturbance of the life-pattern with its hierarchy of vital forces, and a degradation of the personality.

In the final analysis, we may ask : why is this confusion introduced into the divine order by the practice of self-abuse to be regarded as more serious than other kinds of confusion ? Why shou'd disorder in the essential purpose of the organs of sex be more sinful than disorder in the use of other organs, say for example, the mouth when it is used to utter words contradicting the law of love ? Why should this particular form of egoism be more immoral than another ? Why is this regression and disturbance of the true life-pattern more important than a host of other omissions and escapisms in our daily life ? Such questions as these, which are frequently brought up, seem to be worthy of honest, serious, unprejudiced consideration.

Subjective Guilt

I must repeat that this is not my field of work : I do not propose to enter upon moral and theological discussions. Much has already been said and written on this matter by those to whose province it belongs. I will confine myself to putting forward certain mental and spiritual considerations which urge themselves upon the psychotherapist and are of importance in determining the limits of personal guilt. These are offered as the modest contribution of a layman to this problem.

At the same time, I feel that I should offer a hint to other laymen. It has been my experience that many people do not realise that the Church distinguishes between an objective grave sin, and a subjective grave sin. Fleckenstein has suggested that we should make a clear distinction between the concept " grave sin," as an objective fact, and a " mortal sin " as a wrong act in subjective sense, carrying with it spiritual death. This seems to me a happy terminological solution.

According to our doctrine, a mortal sin is a grave sin committed with clear knowledge and free will. The really decisive point is therefore subjective. It is the mental and spiritual attitude ; the act of the mind. The essence of such an act is defined in classical

terms as *tota aversio a Deo completa*, complete effective turning away
from God. It carries with it separation from God, and death, like
the *non serviam* of Lucifer or the rebellion of the tribal heads who
wished to be gods themselves. It is the spiritual act that decides
and *not* the actual deed itself. This was made clear by Christ Himself, who stated that he who lusted after a woman had already
committed adultery in his heart ; that was the decisive thing, not
the act.

Our investigation is therefore concerned with the state of mind :
to what extent is one who practises self-abuse limited in his clarity
of knowledge and his freedom of will ?

I would like to say in advance that psychotherapists frequently
come across neurotic cases where self-abuse is practised, and a
limitation of responsibility must be assumed as part of the psychic
illness. It is not to be denied that self-abuse can be practised
with conscious purpose and freedom of will ; but I have never
come across such a case. But is not every genuine onanist suffering from psycho-physical infantilism, a species of spiritual immaturity looked upon as diminishing the weight of guilt ? In
general terms, what is the position with respect to clear knowledge
and freedom of the will ? Medical science tells us that all states of
sexual tension have a detrimental and inhibitive influence upon the
cerebral centre of mental processes. The urge towards detumescence—expulsion of the semen—can be far stronger than the
instinct of self-preservation. Everyone who has watched deer,
otherwise so shy, during the period of sexual heat knows this. All the
caution otherwise so manifest is forgotten ; there is no thought of
anything but the instinctive urge. Thought can be wholly dominated by the sexual urge, and then clear insight becomes more and
more impossible.

The psychologist can make the most astounding observations in
this sphere. It is quite likely, for example, that a man in a certain
state of sexual excitement will not be held back from sexual intercourse even by the knowledge that his partner suffers from a
venereal disease which is undoubtedly infectious. In exactly the
same way, a man given to self-abuse will go on doing it, even if he
fully believes in the severe injury to health which he has been
told will ensue. How much less will he be restrained by the much
less tangible idea of spiritual injury. In truth he is quite unable to
grasp the moral weight of what he does ; he simply does not
realise the mortal sin.

From my own observation I would say that the majority of those
who practice self-abuse or extra-matrimonial intercourse would
utterly repudiate the idea that they do anything contrary to the will

of God or desire to separate themselves from Him. They are not able to think clearly in this field, so completely is it dominated by the sexual urge. The reality of God seems very dim and remote, even when He is thought about at all. *Omne peccatum opponitur prudentiae*, one might say, altering only slightly the phrasing of St. Thomas Aquinas.

A backward glimpse of the situation corroborates this view. How often has one heard an onanist say that the first idea that came into his mind, after experiencing a sensation of relief was : " What have I done ? How could I do it ? " He does not even know how he came to do it, because he did not want to do so. The clouding of the brain centres disappears after the loss of sexual tension ; and, now that his thought is clear and free, he is unable to appreciate the preceding state of mind.

The situation as regards freedom of will is the same. In the field of mind, the processes are subject to domination by elements surging from the subconscious, forces of an instinctive nature bringing the personality more or less under compulsion. These subconscious motives give rise to an urge towards self-abuse, and the conscious will is not strong enough to check them ; thus a position arises in which we can hardly speak of freedom of will.

The spiritual director will seek to clarify the problem with a question such as : " Did you *want* to commit this act ? " In most cases, he will receive the answer that the urge from the instinctive forces was too strong for him, in spite of a desire to resist ; or that, at a time when he was not on his guard, he just " slipped into it," almost without realising what he was doing.

At this point we have to reckon with a set of circumstances encountered in psychotherapy, more especially with those suffering from excessive scrupulosity—cases verging on compulsory neurosis. They know that the consent of the will is necessary to establish mortal sin. They ask themselves if, after all, they did not consent ? It is true that a consent of the will is required if an act is to take place at all, yet we cannot regard this as a free decision ; it is rather a giving way, a surrender of the weaker when faced with superior forces. Such types rightly allege weakness of will ; but looked upon symptomatically, it is not, in its essence, a motivating weakness. To this question we return later.

Doctors engaged in analytical practice meet with another type : the man who quite consciously answers to the voice of inner conscience with : " No ! " Such a man suffers, as he himself complains, from an evil will and is often quite in despair about his depraved character ; he cannot discover within himself even the very first step towards being a good man—the *will* to be good. An inward compulsory factor, comparable to the " defiance " which is noted in children of a certain age, is often the true explanation of such an attitude. The scope of this book does not enable us to enter upon an examination of the psychology of opposition. It is sufficient at present to state that this oppositional attitude can manifest itself in what we may term " oppositional self-abuse," when the sufferer seeks for individuality and not, as in the " self-abuse as comfort " situation, for love. He seeks to demonstrate his independence by resisting everything of an imperative character. Spiritual directors should understand that in such a case the will may quite consciously accept self-abuse ; and yet, it is not a free will, but a reaction imposed by factors in the unconscious mind. These urges, springing from the depths, can be so compulsory and so completely inaccessible from the level of the conscious mind that the sufferer may be driven to the verge of despair or even of insanity.

Every psychologist knows how many of our daily actions are conditioned by unconscious motives. The moral theologian Froeves is reported to have said in a lecture : " If a man performs ten completely free acts of the will during his entire life, that is a high proportion." Other moralists, however are of the opinion that most acts are *ordinarily* free enough to qualify as human, deliberate, and moral.

Knowledge and will are naturally more seriously weakened in the case of an act which, by its nature, belongs to the earth-bound sphere of life and is in opposition to the conscious and spiritual sphere ; an act, moreover, that takes place when cool reason is more or less confused. Many spiritual directors take the view that sins against the sixth commandment very seldom take place unless there is some limitation of knowledge and free will. On the one hand, in my opinion, importance should be attached to the opinion of those theologians who hold that one should not seek and find mortal sins in every quarter, for they are not easily possible to a Christian who is concerned with God ; and on the other, one must not make too little of the venial sins, for they too *are* sins—offences against God. In this fashion the door is barred against laxity. It is not events in the physical field which—as Angermair says—are the cause of sin, not a weak but innocent will ; for sin is due essentially to the evil *will*, acting from free personal decision, in so far as such a decision is possible in the case of self-abuse. For we can safely say that this practice is, in most cases, a symptom of spiritual immaturity, a state of mind which does not provide the conditions for genuine free decision.

If, in a specific instance, the spiritual director, or it may be the penitent himself, arrives at the conviction that this is not a case of mortal sin, but of a more or less serious venial sin, then the logical consequence would be that confession is not obligatory before each Communion, especially in the case of daily Communion.   The understanding priest will give his specific permission especially when the penitent is a regular communicant.   The Sacrament of the Eucharist is not a prize awarded for saintliness but, as the post-communion prayers state, a means of bettering ourselves and a help given in our imperfection.

Moralists frequently put forward the view that habitual self-abuse is obviously not a grave sin ; yet there must have been a beginning and the first time the onanist must have acted with consciousness and free will. Then it was a mortal sin. In the preceding sections we have dealt with the factors which cause this act. I do not think that the considerations brought forward would indicate that the onanist —whatever his age—began with a free will and clear consciousness. This is certainly the case with the practice in early childhood of quasi-self-abuse, as we have described it. Who would here speak of sin ? This applies whether such childish acts are the outcome of play, or result, in a more significant fashion, from some maladjust-ment of the child. In these cases the child is not a " sinner ; " the term would be more fittingly applied to the adults in charge of him.

The same line of argument is valid when we consider the self-abuse of early puberty, provoked as it is by factors linked with the biological development, with the upsurging forces of nature. The vicious boy is a child who suffers from the activity of forces he cannot understand ; a child in need of all the help we can give. This is most certainly the case with self-abuse arising from neurotic conditions, since here there is no question of sin, but of psychic illness.   Where there is question of self-abuse from necessity, we cannot speak either of a loss of contact between the higher and lower levels of personality, or of moral depravity. In as far as the term necessity is justifiably employed, we must admit a limitation of free decision and thus exclude the notion of a mortal sin. If the need is merely imagined, we may look upon it as a case of confirmed onanism.

I should be grieved if my readers were to misinterpret the fore-going in the sense that there can be no question of sin where self-abuse is concerned, and that one may therefore continue the practice with a good conscience. This is most certainly not the case. The various psychological limitations brought forward were solely concerned with subjective mortal sin.   Let us consider self-abuse stemming from neurotic states, where the habit is a symptom : is the sufferer wholly innocent of his wrong attitude, even if it be a species of illness ? It is not easy to separate guilt from " fate." It is certainly true that a neurotic character is induced in the child by disposition, education, and environmental factors. The fourth factor, self-education, as experience tells us, is not actually equal to the other three in power. Accordingly, in most cases, the attempt to reform and rightly develop the character, even if honestly and sincerely attempted, is not successful. Nevertheless, the subject feels that he is not wholly innocent in respect of his infantile fault. A final thought in this connection seems to me to be worthy of serious consideration. Since we are beings informed with souls, is it not illogical if we regard expressions of our sinful nature in the bodily and sexual field as more grave than those of a purely spiritual nature: for example, lovelessness, egoism, jealousy, mendacity, or pride ?

The Problem of Guilt

Much excellent material has been put forward by Angermair and Fleckenstein* on the problem of care of souls and methods of help in this difficult sphere. We cannot, at this point, take up their arguments, and many of my readers are doubtless already acquainted with them. It will be sufficient to mention that the psychological and pedagogical factors are strongly emphasised. There is little sympathy with what may be called the " panel-patient " routine of some confessors who get through a large number of confessions in a short time. Each individaul must receive careful personal attention.

It is often said that the time for this attention is lacking ; that, on Saturday night, for example, a great number wait to make their confession and have to be dealt with. It is my view, on the other hand, that if I find that three times in succession I fail to reach my turn because, out of twenty who are waiting only five can be heard, then I must willy-nilly make up my mind to go to confession at a less busy time. Perhaps things are made too easy for the penitent, and this does scant justice to the psychological importance and dignity of the Sacrament.

The individual care of souls is undoubtedly more difficult since it requires psychological knowledge and a certain gift for entering into the mind of another. It will not be enough to prepare an excellent address for the day in question. Quickness of mind and concentration will be needed to discover the exact spot where the individual can best be approached. Only in this way will the spiritual director be not only a priest, but also a true shepherd of souls. Knowledge of the human soul on the intellectual plane will help, but is not enough ; the chief role will be played by the heart, which must remain open to receive the right guidance.

*See Appendix for excerpts from their writings on the subject.

Many good Catholics leave the confessional unsatisfied, unmoved, and without feeling of liberation. This is related not only to the fact. that the Sacrament, in all its consequences, is not taken seriously enough, but quite often to the expectation of *feeling*, and not only believing, that the father confessor is the representative of God. The layman looks for Christ in the priest ; for a man who will know what is *not* said and take into consideration all that lies. between the spoken words. Knowledge of psychic reactions, trends, and relationships will make it possible for the priest, in his office as shepherd of souls, to follow Him who read souls like an open book. Then he will not allow himself to be blinded by the external act ; but will often hold an opinion contrary to that which seems. clear to the superficial mind. He will condemn, when the self-righteous see no sin, and forgive when the public sinner, according to the letter of the law, would be exposed to death by stoning. In this connection see the vitally important book of August Adam,. *Christus und die Frau* (Verlag Ettal, 1950).

One of the chief reasons for unsatisfactory confessions would seem to be that essential matters were not brought forward, even though the penitent had confessed all sins. In this connection, self-abuse forms a pointer for related problems. One must take the trouble to collect together everything of which the habit may be an expression. With the knowledge of what form of self-abuse is in question,. which may involve the asking of a simple question, the shepherd of souls can say plainly to the penitent that at this or that point in his life there is probably something else that is wrong. He thus. brings the conversation around to the vitally important matter that still needs clearing up : e.g., how do things stand with the penitent's relationships to his fellow men, to the community, and to. his profession or occupation ? How does he stand with himself—i.e.,. what meaning and purpose has his life: what is his attitude towards. God: is his religion becoming deeper and more vital ? Does he occupy himself with the things of God, and is his religious life developing ?

In this way the centre of gravity is removed from the act of self-abuse (the symptom) and placed where it belongs, at the root. The penitent will seek to order his life anew instead of exhausting his. spiritual energies in a vain struggle against his " vice ". Modern Catholic writers are at one in saying that it is a great error to speak. of self-abuse as a vice. The authors of the *Cahiers Laënnec*, for example, are concerned that the phenomenon of self-abuse should be integrated in a general study of the character and psychology of the individual and approached from that angle.* If the significance of the habit is overemphasised, the task of overcoming it may become.

*See *New Problems in Medical Ethics, Series I* (Mercier Press).

doubtful, and complications may ensue leading, possibly, to compulsory self-abuse. Threats and stern prohibitions—even if they have a metaphysical basis—are not adequate to restore the lost balance of personality ; and only when this balance is discovered and maintained will the individual be able to develop and to resist the temptations that assail him before sexuality can be fulfilled in a genuine love.

When the self-abuser has been brought by adroit guidance from the priest to place the main emphasis upon basic causes—upon the wrong life-attitude and not upon the symptom (the practice itself)—he will not be so deeply ashamed to come back to his confessor with the same statement. We know how the overstressing of the habit and the sense of shame that follows, drive young people, and adults also, from one confessor to another—to " someone who does not yet know me "—or, in other cases, leads to a total falling away from confession. The right and necessary kind of guidance—so essential in these cases—is thus made impossible. Sometimes it may be wise to tell the penitent right away that he cannot expect to be liberated almost at once from this habit but that he needs a reorganisation of his character, in which aim the spiritual director will help him. It is true that this takes time and trouble.

The psychotherapist knows a considerable number of onanists in whose cases he would like to suggest to the priest that he might well consider the wisdom of omitting altogether the mention by the penitent of this habit in the confessional, even though the latter inwardly repents. For the continual repetition of the same thing tends to build up a fixation, as well as being discouraging. It might be more advisable to make a point of confessing only when there is *no* sin : " I do not want you to mention your habit of self-abuse again, until you have succeeded in not doing it at all in the period between two confessions." This is a little psychological spur, of which one may well make use.

The young often practice self-abuse without a trace of guilt : most of these do not belong to the " depraved " who have silenced conscience on the well-known principle that " conscience spoils pleasure, so away with conscience ! " In the early days of puberty, quite a number of children practice this habit entirely without the sense of guilt ; the same thing happens with self-abuse in early childhood. If, for example, a little girl of four plays with her sexual organs in the hope that she will thus get the same organ as her brother, we have what Freud calls " penis envy," and this practice may lead to self-abuse. This hardly falls within the field of morals. Many children indulge in self-abuse and even in sexual intercourse, without any feeling of sin.

A patient told me that, when he was seven years old, he used to stand against a window, naked, and squeeze his penis between the thighs, thus obtaining a sensation of pleasure which he regarded, however, as a kind of pain : there was no feeling of guilt. When he was eight, his sister encouraged him to have sexual intercourse with a friend of hers ; he had no feelings of pleasure and no sense of guilt. At age fourteen he began to indulge in self-abuse, about once a week, regarding it as something on much the same level as urinating —to be done in private. Later, in religious instruction, he was told it was a sinful thing ; although now feeling he was committing a grave sin and struggling against it, he went on with the habit and it actually became much more frequent. The result was a profound feeling of discouragement. Previously, he had been a leader of a group of small boys and was very active in this and in his religious duties ; but now he was afraid of going to confession and became more and more lax in his religious life.

Another boy practised self-abuse at first wholly without any sense of guilt. It seemed to him a natural mode of relief. Not until he was nineteen did he discover, through a priest, that it was sinful. By making a great effort of will he broke off the habit. Its place was taken however by various disorders : his right hand became cramped and he could not write (an expression of compulsion affecting the member used in his self-abuse), and it was obvious that his psychic development was at a standstill. Many psychologists (for instance Gebsattel) are of the opinion that the young practise self-abuse without any idea of guilt, unless they have been told of its " deadly sinfulness." At more advanced ages, the feeling of guilt may come quite of its own accord ; an inner voice says that it is now time for the spirit to deal with these states of sexual disturbance. A conquest of the higher spiritual man by the forces surging up from the lower world of sex instinct is then felt to be shameful, and feelings of guilt develop.

This change of mind is revealed also in other fields of life : the receptive egocentric type of love is appropriate to a small child's stage of development ; but, if at a later age he still clings to it, such an attitude is not appropriate and is a sign of something wrong.

Day-dreams are right and normal for the young child, but a retention of this habit into and beyond puberty is not normal and is again a danger signal.

Self-abuse is in accordance with normal development at the introverted stage of early puberty, for it is a symptom of immaturity. But in the years when extroversion is expected, a continuation of the habit is *not* appropriate, and is an indication that development is not taking place as it should, that there is a fixation at the stage of early puberty. Accordingly, feelings of guilt, which did not previously exist, come into being.

These feelings of guilt are often quite overwhelming and can assume various forms. We will take up three of the more important types, for they are of considerable significance in the spiritual care of these cases. As the first of these, we may consider the guilt consciousness implanted by a purely formal training, often surviving from early childhood when the immature individual acquired a sense of guilt, a " bad conscience " through expecting punishment for this or that. This type of feeling has no necessary connection with real conscience and often manifests itself when there is no question of guilt in the sight of God. In these cases, the young person exhausts himself in self-reproaches, following in the footsteps of his educator who used to reproach him ; for he treats himself as he was treated when a child, and, accordingly, when faced with some lapse, he is apt to say to himself : " You need not be surprised that you have fallen again. With you nothing goes right. You know only too well what sort of a chap you are—even as a child you were always doing this or that." One hears the nagging voice of the teacher, full of discouragement, forgiving and forgetting nothing.

This sort of " bad conscience " with its self-reproaches will not disappear after absolution or, if it does, will reappear at the first opportunity. It does not consist in any real guilt before God, personally accepted and confessed, but in a guilty feeling towards father or mother as the case may be, where their attitude towards their child was far from being, as it should have been, that of God's stewards. The sense of guilt is liable to be very active with people who were educated along very authoritarian lines and subjected to much moralising ; and it will be absent when those in charge let the child have its own way—a course not to be recommended. As we have said in another place, it is one of the problems of a good education to do away with the element of training as soon as possible and replace it by the right type of education, namely *self*-education in freedom and responsibility. A vague consciousness of guilt, *not of any specific sin*, is found with special frequency in the field of sex, as a result of prevalent false shame, and wrong education in sexual matters. It causes discouragement and not only leads too easily to self-abuse, but makes it much more difficult to overcome the practice, since it amounts to a negative fixation.

The priest will possibly take note of the immaturity and lack of freedom in the psychology of the penitent, and lead him very gently and gradually to a criticism of his own conscience and the manner of its formation ; for so long as the formal and imposed type of conscience is dominant, there cannot be any question of real conscience.

The self-reproaches take on a twofold character, for at the same time the penitent has a streak of rebellion in his mind—not actually against God but against his educator. He cannot adopt a clear attitude towards personal guilt before God and cannot accept the idea of sin, with all its consequences, which should lead to repentance and confession. Accordingly, in a very paradoxical fashion, a desperate feeling of being cast out goes hand in hand with a defiant pride, with the fully conscious denial of " bad will, " of which we have spoken. There is a consciousness somewhere of the wrongness of this rebellious spirit, of the lack of true self-love from which the subject suffers. In similar fashion, feelings of inferiority can accompany self-glorification.

Together with the feeling of guilt imposed from without, which is not genuine, we find two types of real guilt-consciousness, having their roots in conscience. The first is *definite*. It arises spontaneously after the wrong action and is dissolved after absolution : I know, in this case, my definite guilt in the sight of God and adopt towards it a clear-cut attitude in humility, repentance, and good intention. It is a feeling of guilt in a well-defined field of moral law. I know that I have sinned against the express commandment of God. No further comment is here needed as to this feeling (or knowledge) of guilt.

The other type of guilt-consciousness is less well known. It does not arise as a definite knowledge of guilt : it is rather a vague *sensation* of guilt. This is a much wider concept than that of " sin," and thus it often continues after confession. This feeling is genuine. It does not refer to a subjective guilt in the sight of God, but to an objective guilt independent of any subjective wrong touching the character or capacity. That is to say, it is directed not towards the *sinful act* for which one feels guilty and responsible, but towards a *wrong attitude of mind*, which may be due to external causes, such as disposition, milieu, or education. For this, the individual is responsible only in a limited sense ; it may even in many cases be impossible for him to overcome this, despite every effort. In such a case, the voice of conscience is directed not towards the moral side of life but towards the ethical attitude upon which the individual bases his life. The feeling of guilt remains after absolution, in so far as it is realised that the positive life-task that one owes to God, according to man's inborn nature, has not been adequately mastered. The guilt feeling is not in the least concerned with the problem of whether or not this fulfilment is possible in view of limitations imposed by character.

If self-abuse, now practised without a sense of guilt, gives rise later—with or without influence from outside—to feelings of guilt, these are either of a moral order, in so far as a clear knowledge of guilt in the sight of God has been obtained, or they are ethical, since in the self-abuse it is felt that there is a failure to fulfil the life-purpose given by God to human beings by virtue of their humanity. It is more often the case that both of these forms occur together. This twofold guilt-feeling plays a large part in causing the practice of self-abuse to weigh so heavily on the conscience of the subject.

For the shepherd of souls this vague consciousness of guilt has a further deep significance. On the one hand, he can take it as a signal to accept original sin as a fact, in a spirit of humility, and as a call to the betterment of the general state of imperfection. On the other hand, he must take it into careful consideration in his words to the penitent.

To take an example : here is an onanist in whose case the priest is justified in assuming that his self-abuse is a sign of neurosis or of some psychopathic condition. The victim is in the grip of what he regards a mortal sin, which has separated him from the world, destroyed his values, and made him unfit for life. Under these circumstances, the priest feels himself able to say, with good reason: " In your case this is not a sin, it is an illness. I take the whole responsibility in this case and tell you you are not sinning, so long as your will is good. I advise you to turn your attention to the tasks of daily life." The onanist will then leave the confessional with a feeling of liberation. However, his bad habit is not overcome and it may happen that he will do the same thing again very shortly. He knows it is not a sin; for this he has the statement of the priest. Nevertheless, feelings of guilt begin to plague him again. He asks himself what it all means. He feels in his conscience that this *is* a mortal sin. Was the priest wrong after all ? In this way confidence in the father confessor may be heavily damaged.

In such a case, it is the ethical guilt-feeling that is asserting itself, not the moral. As we have said, self-abuse is a symptom, indicating neurotic maladjustment—a sign of infantilism. This must be known to the priest and it is good that he should explain it to the penitent. For confidence in the spiritual adviser and the feeling of being understood are basic factors in helping the penitent.

THE TREATMENT OF SELF-ABUSE

Historical Outline

A BRIEF review of what has been done historically in the way of treating this practice may be of some value. In 1710, Becker, an English doctor, wrote a treatise, *Onanism or the Shocking Sin of*

Self-Abuse. He advised a policy of frightening young people to keep them away from it. The best means of prevention was marriage. In 1769, Tissot, a Lausanne doctor, published *L'Onanisme ou Dissertation sur les Maladies produites par la Masturbation.* He represented onanism as a disease, accompanied by fearful consequences. He recommended baths, exercise in the fresh air, regulation of sleep, distraction, and liberation from loneliness. Despite this good advice, he did a vast amount of harm through his false account of the consequences of self-abuse.

In 1786, S. G. Vogel, a British court physician and military doctor, enlarged upon the means suggested by Tissot and recommended good reading, prayer, and, in addition, the use of mechanical means, the latter included so-called infibulation (a method of sewing up the organs). By way of prophylaxis, he mentioned exercise, avoidance of alcohol, and gradual enlightenment. In 1894, the Breslau eye specialist, H. Cohn, suggested enlightenment as the best method of dealing with the habit. In 1898, Rohleder, a Leipzig specialist in sexual diseases, published a monograph entitled *Die Masturbation* (last edition 1921) in which he gathered together a large body of material, and reached the conclusion that self-abuse is a medical matter ; he did not deal with the pedagogical aspect. In 1929, M. Hodan published a work with the title : "Onanism Is Neither a Vice Nor an Illness." In contrast to earlier writers, he denied all ill effects upon health, other than those that might be caused by a feeling of guilt induced by public opinion. His only suggestion on educational lines was : *Laisser faire, laisser aller.*

Since the turn of the century, a series of articles dealing with this problem have appeared in various medical journals, such as contributions by Meirowsky and Neisser who favoured enlightenment on sexual matters ; while Posner and von Gruber stressed the educational aspect, the latter believing that self-abuse could be overcome by the development of conscience, devotion to duty, self-control, voluntary asceticism, the cultivation of a sense of honour and of personal responsibility. H. Pezold, in 1933, put forward the view that psychotherapy was the sole means of dealing with the problem. Thus, during the last twenty-five years or so, we observe a new evaluation of the psychological aspects, with a decline in the idea that self-abuse is a disease ; at the same time, the educational factors received more attention. From about 1920 onwards, we find an extensive literature on the problem as viewed psychologically, and we note distinctions between the various forms of self-abuse. We may mention such names as Spranger, Ch. Buhler, W. Stern, W. Hoffmann, and E. Stern. The study of psychopathology provides us with important new contributions :

V. Kafka in his *Sexualpädagogik* (1932) distinguishes between the habit in those who have reached maturity and in those who have not, as well as between normal and neuropathic subjects. With neurotics, the neurosis is the object of treatment, not the habit as such. Schwarz held the same views (*Sexualpathologie*, 1935).

E. Benjamin looked upon onanism as a typical oppositional reaction. The analytical psychologists believe that the most important thing is to liberate the victims of the habit from the feeling of guilt, and frequently they go so far as to say, " Continue the practice as much as you like." Individual psychology adopts the line that the cure of onanism consists in bringing the subject back into the life of the community. It makes a special point of the antithesis between the will to power and the community sense.

In the educational field, the chief stress is laid upon the formation of character : accordingly it is recognised that the chief means to adopt are distraction of the mind, the development of a proper sense of shame, occupation of all the faculties, building up of the will, and faith in ideals. In this group we have such writers as Roetger, Bauer, Sailer, Hirchser, Dursch, Ohler, and Stolz, all of whom derive their experience mainly from the care of souls in a pedagagogical sense. As Sailer writes : " Religion is the basic principle of all cure ; it is the medicine of medicines ; it is the healing power in every means of healing." W. Foerster, Schroeler, C. Hofmann, Schneider, von Rodner, Rohden, and Muckermann have all dealt with the care of souls in this spiritual sense. I agree with the opinion of C. Hofmann that a talk with the onanist outside the confessional is of vital importance. Schneider believes that a talk directed towards strengthening the basic life-purpose is a first-rate method of prevention.

Psychiatry and psychotherapy have, through their exploration of the depths of the soul, made particularly valuable contributions to our knowledge of self-abuse and its treatment. It is strongly emphasised by means of material drawn from a host of unfortunate experiences that all means likely to cause damage to the spirit, especially guilt and anxiety neuroses, should be most carefully avoided. E. Bleuler and Th. Ziehen looked upon self-abuse as a symptom of a neurasthenic or psychopathic constitution—the concept of neurosis was not then in customary use.

Hattingberg called onanism the commonest of all the monosymptomatic neuroses. This opinion carries with it all the therapeutic consequences : " In strongly marked cases, systematic psychotherapy is the only thing that can help ; psychoanalysis is often most effective."

Kronfeld, Kahn, and Villinger advise taking no notice of self-abuse in small children : to talk with them, calm them and bring about a change of surroundings are the best means of treating them. In the case of older children, the main thing is to strengthen self-confidence and bring about distraction from the habit, in both the physical and mental fields, while cultivating hygiene of the imagination. Most essential, in my own view, is the advice of the psycho-analyst Meng, to the effect that the best preventive of self-abuse is good parents—cheerful and kind, but neither too tender nor too strict.

Summing up, we may say that for a long time a one-sided medical viewpoint, intermingled with many errors, held the field. Later on, it was generally recognised that onanism was not a disease but a symptom of failure in the development of the personality as a whole, revealing weaknesses in character and in the attitude towards life. The treatment of self-abuse is, in the main, an affair of the educator involving reform and re-education of the personality. In difficult cases, psychotherapeutic treatment is to be recommended.

External Aids

We have already, in the course of this study, dealt in several places with appropriate aids. In the following section, we will take up one or two special viewpoints not yet, or not yet adequately, dealt with. In the first place, there is the question : Are there any external aids of value in the overcoming of the habit ? Doctors are accustomed to hearing this asked. It has become clear, in the foregoing, that the root of self-abuse is to be found in the interior life of the soul and should be tackled there ; nevertheless, there are external aids capable of helping the work of education. A number of authors emphasise the importance of a diet that is not stimulating and not rich in albumen. That tea, coffee, and all that develops a craving, will tend to expose an unstable character to the craving for self-abuse can hardly be doubted. It is therefore desirable that those in question should refrain from alcohol and nicotine in particular. Experience teaches us that young people who do not control their craving for these will suffer a corresponding diminution in their powers of moral resistance.

Many writers point out the necessity for a *hardening* of the body and recommend such measures as airy, cool, and hard beds, early and prompt rising in the mornings, sport and gymnastics in the evening, and rubbing down with cold water. It is maintained that such hardening of the body will be followed by a strengthening of the will.

The various operative methods which have been tried in the past are to be rejected. Amongst them is infibulation, supposed to make the male organ non-susceptible to irritations ; circumcision, which is quite useless for this purpose ; and even castration, to be condemned as immoral since, in contrast to self-abuse, it strikes a real blow at the forces of life and constitutes a completely unjustifiable interference with the order of nature ; and bleeding from the veins, the sole effect of which could be to produce weakness in general. Even cauterisation of certain genital points has been suggested ; I am not aware of any success along these lines.

The attempt to treat onanism by medicinal means is of limited effect : sedatives can diminish the sexual tension, and tonics can strengthen the general condition of the body, thus promoting the moral forces making for resistance. In the case of self-abuse before sleep, I have had good results from the use of sleeping drugs : the mere fact that the subject knows that now he is not dependent upon self-abuse as a means of inducing sleep, but can use the sleeping medicine if needful, often releases the onanist from his habit. In general, however, we must not forget that such means must be employed as sparingly as possible. It is certainly not in this way alone that the trouble can be mastered.

Influence brought to bear upon the personal surroundings of the subject is more important than medicines and goes nearer to the true causes. Often a word of enlightenment to the parents, educators, or employers of the subject can correct wrong attitudes on their part and remove influences tending to encourage the practice. In the case of schoolchildren, one can sometimes make use of the *other* children in order to remove a state of isolation on the part of the child in question and thus liberate him from the practice ; and a personal and truly human word spoken by a teacher may often prove to be a turning point in the child's trouble.

The choice of profession or occupation should not be neglected. We know that very many young people do not take up the type of work suited to their disposition. In consequence, they often fall into a state of difficulty and conflict with the outer world and with themselves. The depression and disappointment apt to follow is frequently an occasion inducing self-abuse. Thus, it is well worth while—not only in relation to the problem of onanism, but for the subject's whole life—to consult an experienced adviser on occupational problems.

Fighting against Self-Abuse

We know from the foregoing material that every direct struggle against onanism is apt to have the opposite effect to that desired. Even prayer when specifically directed against the habit is—as we know from numerous reports—usually ineffective : this is especially the case when it has been advised that the subject should pray that the temptation may pass away. Every spiritual director knows that this often aggravates the trouble. For all the time the attention is turned *towards* the practice ; the subject keeps his mind fixed continually upon the very thing he wishes to avoid.

Religious power is, without doubt, of the first importance. If the victim of self-abuse can succeed in practising true religious meditation and prayer, it is a matter-of-course that his tension and " temptation " can be overcome in this manner. For that is a real value taking the place of a substitute satisfaction. But it is vital that the onanist should direct his energies, not against his habit, but in a positive sense towards religion. It must be no mere negation : " No, I will not do that ; " but: " No, I am determined to do this *other* thing ! " In this way alone can true freedom from the servitude of instinct be achieved, by a free decision of the will in favour of values that are within his grasp. With those to whom religion is not a living thing with real values, the path of prayer cannot lead to the desired goal.

When educators try to preserve children from this habit by means of threats, there is a danger that the child can suffer a permanent distortion of sexual life. Thus it is well known that the threat to cut " it " off, can lead easily to the co-called " castration complex," which may throw a shadow across the entire future life.

The Triumph of the Will

In my practice I frequently meet with people who tell me that when young they had trouble with self-abuse. But when they discovered that it was a sin and an unclean thing, they ceased at once to have anything more to do with it. At first sight, one might well think this is the ideal method. In reality, this is far from being true ; for experience—more especially that of the psychotherapist—shows us that these " victors " are in reality the conquered. They have done no more than exchange one symptom of a wrong life-attitude for another, and much *worse* one, for it drove them, finally, to consult a doctor, since in one way or another their lives were wrecked.

He who realises inwardly that the path of self-abuse is an error and cannot lead anywhere, and sets himself to find another and better way of fulfilment, will be the most likely to overcome the habit. He will not try to make use of energetic will power to suppress what is a symptom, but develop beyond it to real and worthwhile aims. But the " victor " has in no way changed his wrong attitude ; he has merely removed the danger signal warning him that he must reform his life. Hence two dangers result : in the first place, he has deprived himself of the mirror reflecting his error and is only too likely to think that now he is all right ; secondly, the suppression of the self-abuse, leads as a rule to suppression of the sexual in general, together with the vital impulses rooted in the basic instinctive urge. This brings about a stultification in the further development of his life. The personality is split into two parts, body and soul, and we have a poisoning of the springs of the emotional life. Hence the widespread phenomenon of lovelessness and self-righteousness amongst these " acrobats of the will." This explains, also, the organised but sterile and unorganic life of such types, more especially in the field of religion, together with a lack of warm love for fellow human beings. It is understandable that, amongst these people we find a high proportion who live under the shadow of compulsion : men and women who are spiritually and physically inhibited, who do their duty painfully but without vital warmth and energy. They are the victims of their own " victory," withered up and resigned.

We have other cases where the use of the will does not succeed. They seek a spiritual director and say somewhat as follows: " I know that a mere struggling against the habit does not help. But I do not know of any other way of overcoming it." This opens the way to a discussion with the adviser or teacher, who should then try to find out what lies behind the practice. Is it obstinacy or defiance ? Is it comfort that is sought ? Is the subject egocentric and out of touch with his fellow humans ? Or is it, perhaps, a case of what we have called self-abuse by necessity ? What caused the subject to begin this practice ? Is it a symptom of some inward disordered state, a reaction in the face of outward troubles or a mere empty habit ? How different will one's attitude be towards the boy who says : " My friends tell me that it is abnormal not to practise self-abuse ; and I wanted to be normal. Thus I began the practice although I had no desire to do so "—as compared with that adopted towards another who is completely overwhelmed with the sense of having committed a mortal sin.

Each case must be considered separately. No case must be forced into some preconceived pattern. Individual psychology is always the right method.

I feel bound to support Gügler when he demands from the priest that " in matters relating to onanism, and in general to sexual psychology and pedagogy, he should have an adequate knowledge," because " adolescents, in particular, will always be able to unburden themselves most easily to one who understands their peculiar state of mental and moral confusion, when they perceive that the educator is able to reveal to them the relationships existing between conditions determined by development, and qualities of character, thus indicating the path of salvation. In such conditions, the victim of self-abuse will, in most cases, exhibit the utmost confidence in his helper."

This relationship of confidence is often of decisive importance, for it represents the first bridge leading from isolation back to social life. While the helper must reveal an inward authority, it is well, on the other hand, if he can let the sufferer know that he *himself* has, perhaps, at one time, been through similar difficulties. The young person will then perceive at once that he is not, after all, such a bad fellow and that one can go through all these things and emerge victorious. This gives courage and new hope.

I remember a priest who told me that an adolescent came to him and complained: " I never can manage to get things into the proper order," whereupon the priest replied, laconically, "Neither can I." He then explained that, in consequence of our original sin, the right order had been destroyed and that it should be our lifelong task to work for the re-establishment of order ; and that the man who thinks his life is rightly ordered is the furthest away from success in this task.

Liberation from Isolation

We have already recognised that many forms of self-abuse are signs that the subject finds himself in conflict with those around him. This may be because of the oppositional attitude characteristic of a certain stage of growth, or because of a lack of proper contact, due to faulty educational or environmental influences. Or it may be a type of isolation conditioned by special circumstances, or by some individual peculiarity.

In these cases, it will be wise either to teach the young person to understand himself and thus counter his tendency to react against his human environment, or to seek to exercise a direct influence upon the environment. Not long ago we made an experiment in a school : there was a little girl of eleven who practised self-abuse continually, even during school hours whenever the teacher was not looking. The teacher was quite unable to meet the situation. She tried being strict and being kind : nothing was of any use. The class was then requested, by means of written answers, to state who was the best liked and the least liked among all the pupils, and it came out that this particular girl was the least popular of all. The teacher then took the most popular one, explained to her how it stood with the other little girl, how lonely she was and how little liked, and asked her to take an interest in her with a view to helping her. At the same time, she set the two side-by-side in the class.

When the other children saw that their most respected and popular schoolmate associated with the lonely child, the latter acquired quite a new status in the eyes of the class. They ceased to turn their backs upon her and very soon she found her way back to a social life with the other girls. She was further encouraged by being given small tasks with responsibility, and by achieving success in various other ways ; and, in quite a short time, not only did her bad practices cease but her school work showed a marked improvement. Unfortunately it was not possible to influence the child's mother—a woman of an abandoned type. This example might be imitated in one way or another with success. Side by side with the attempt to discover the sources of discouragement and isolation, we can take into account a possible change of environment, the employment of the subject in social tasks, and the sharing of responsibility in connection with some group, or possibly bringing him into social contact with people of the opposite sex, to encourage him through the experience of real neighbourly love and his own exercise of it. This is a practical application of the truths dealt with in our book on marriage, in the section entitled " Learning to Love."

It is well to begin with the question : What is the onanist looking for ? what object has he in view ? This can be followed by the simple question : Does he get what he seeks ? Not through reasoning only, but from personal experience, the subject must recognise that he is pursuing a path which can never lead him to the desired goal. He cannot fail to see that he is caught up in a vicious circle of cause and effect which turns perpetually upon itself. He will then be prepared to take stock of his position and look for a better way.

It is our task to point out, with Hesnard, that " sexual pleasure signifies an enrichment of life and is a source of real joy, when it is neither partial nor aberrant, but is raised to the level of *love*, embracing tenderness and self-oblation." The root of the matter is a healthy, positive education in sex, capable of imparting to the victim of self-abuse an affirmative attitude towards his bodily life.

The Positive Basis

In order to render aid to those in mental and spiritual difficulties, it is necessary, not only to recognise what is wrong and disordered ; it is even more important to discover what is *right*, to find healthy elements in the personality of the person in question and make use of these as foundation stones in the rebuilding of his life. If only in a rudimentary form, there is always something good and healthy in everyone who comes seeking help, otherwise why should he want to be helped ? In the case of self-abuse, one can often show in an immediate and concrete fashion that there is something healthy even in the habit itself. This is a legitimate urge—however wrong the means may be—in the direction of love, of individuality, or of some new formation of life. These urges are, for the most part, not consciously present to the sufferer although he may dimly realise their existence. To make them present to his mind will help him to understand his own real aims, not those in any way forced upon him, and this often makes it possible for him to take the decisive step leading to genuine forward development. To become aware of something positive in himself, to glimpse the possibility of a valid personal development, gives encouragement to the adolescent and restores confidence in all that is good within himself. The educator will then strive to build upon this foundation. But he must take care not to demand too much, while assigning tasks fitted to the individual capacity. He will seek to avoid anything likely to lead to failure in the case of the victim of self-abuse, as this may cause depression and a loss of purposefulness. He will also applaud his successful work, in order to give him joy in positive tasks and in trying out his strength. He will speak as little as possible about the habit itself, for the strengthening of the positive urge is the main thing in overcoming it.

Thus by building upon the foundation of all that is right and healthy, liberating energies, and awakening confidence, one will be able to correct a great deal of what is faulty. But this is not enough. One must make a direct attack upon inhibitions, and more especially upon feelings of anxiety and guilt. Together with all that belongs to a right sexual education, a talk on religious lines about the problem of sin will be of value.

In many cases, the teacher may not succeed, without calling in the aid of a competent psychotherapist, in removing false inhibitions which very often have their roots in the unconscious. Finally, I must issue a serious warning against any sort of amateurish experimentation with depth psychology.

Life Aims

We have already spoken of the aims set before the higher erotic life of the young. It is one of the typical signs of youthful neurosis that the adolescent does not succeed in bringing about the spiritual fulfilment that would enable him to perceive that his life must aim at a future goal, towards which he is led by various paths, themselves directed towards more immediate ends. It is well to make him understand that he should *progress* in life, and should beware of remaining fixed upon a lower level. This will help him to make use of his conscious spiritual powers to avoid the dangers of escapism.

A young man who earnestly strove after all that was good before his self-abuse became so firmly established as to form a complex, told me, at a later date, that, when he found himself entangled in a web of sin, he no longer dared to seek after good with the old fervour: " I felt I must first be free from sin—otherwise all was in vain, save the state of grace itself. The feeling of mortal sin quenched all my interior life. The outer picture might seem the same, but within all was hollow. Until to-day—a period of seventeen years—my life has been so spent in defending myself against evil that I have had no energy for doing anything positive. Sometimes I think that the traditional practice of the sixth commandment is a cunning device of the devil, to keep us away from pursuing the good."

This example shows us that, in endeavouring to form the erotic life of the young, we have to take into account such lines of thought as this, and we must recognise that all our educational means work together, that it is always a question of the personality *as a whole*, in the re-education of character.

After the years of early puberty, the onanist is often a character who tries to avoid all difficulties and conflicts. When confronted by two possibilities he always chooses the one demanding the least effort. Let us try to make him see that he must really try to be a man ; that, if he goes on pursuing the easy path, he will remain for ever a nobody. If he wants to become a personality commanding respect, he must cease to avoid difficulty and must learn not to choose the easy path. He should, on the contrary, choose the more difficult path when facing alternatives ; then he has a chance of developing his character.

In this fashion, we try to lead him systematically to the self-education of his will. Many methods of helping him have been suggested. One of the most common is to suggest to the subject that he should remain free from his fault for a week after Communion, until the Communion on the Sunday next but one. Such an exercise in self-control may without doubt be successful in some cases ; but in my opinion one should be very careful about making use of it in the matter of self-abuse ; for, by setting a task in this way, one tends to lay emphasis upon the fault and to cause a fixation. Further-more, the subject will tend to feel that the confessor regards self-abuse as a mortal sin, rendering Communion out of the question. It seems to me better to take another line : " Your practice is quite out of keeping with your present state of maturity." This stim-ulates the self-esteem of the subject and forms a powerful motive for further development. The chivalry of the young may also provide us with a first-rate motive in the building up of self-control. It cannot be aroused too soon. It is very damaging if the mother, or perhaps sisters, spoil the boy by taking over the role of servants attending upon him. This kind of love is a grave danger for a boy given to self-abuse—or one not yet an addict.   The practice recommended by Gügler of denying oneself something otherwise permitted—perhaps sweets or cigarettes—is quite a good thing, if it is carried out voluntarily ; but one must never forget that the right idea is that of *self-control*.

Backsliding

" I won't play any more ! I always lose ! " But the boy who loses can be a good player too, even if his partner in the game is better.   The loser may even be a better player than the winner, but not so strong in competitive spirit or in the will to win, so that he loses after all.   We should encourage the loser by saying : " Try to avoid mistakes which cause you to lose ; learn from them, and try and try again. After a time you will become so strong that you will gain the victory."   And one may add the saying of St. Augustine : " If it should come about that in the last hour you are not the victor, be certain that it can be said you were a great fighter." A fighter for *something*.

When confronted with an attitude of resignation due to un-successful efforts, we must not forget the parable of the fishers : if we caught nothing throughout the night, how can we expect to get any fish during the day ? Yet, by the grace of God, the boat was filled to overflowing. This can apply also to the sudden coming of maturity. But grace presupposes our own natural effort.

Often we experience genuine depressions which attack someone who sees himself failing again and again in some weakness which he has learned to look upon as his central fault, and is therefore particularly anxious to avoid. In the struggle to attain to mental and spiritual mastery, every defeat at the hands of the animal urges provides a new reason to feel truly humble and to recognise how far we are from the desired goal of perfection. While this is indeed a cause for sorrow, we must not give way to depression, for that is to abandon hope and to cut away the ground upon which we should go forward to self-education and a ripening of character.

There are others who do not adopt any special attitude towards their practice of self-abuse. It may be that they refuse to see their defeat, so full are they of a self-righteousness which serves to en-courage natural inertia and to deter them from making the self-educational effort demanded. Or, again, this attitude may be due to rebellion against some outward type of authority to which they were previously subjected, against a continual, " You must ! " or, " You must not ! " An inner relationship to moral law has never

been brought about. A private talk, in which the factors making up
the background are examined, can provide a decisive impetus
leading to a reorientation of mind and heart.

Mental Hygiene

"Sexual hygiene is, to a large extent, hygiene of the imagination:
and this can be said not only of the sexual, but of all psychic hygiene."
Thus writes H. Meng, very truly. At the beginning of this study of
self-abuse, we pointed out the close connection between day-dreams
and this practice. We saw that not only sexually coloured day-
dreams are dubious, but that those quite innocent in themselves are
not without danger ; and that those who indulge in this practice
would do well to return to reality as soon as possible. However, it is
the case with this sort of dreaming, as with other habits—good and
bad—it cannot be altered in a day or two, more especially when, as
with such dreaming, it is a species of addiction that is in question.
Accordingly, those who recognise that they do not act wisely must
take some trouble to reform themselves and must go to work steadily
at their self-reformation. They will often find themselves sliding
back and will have to pull themselves together.

This kind of self-correction should not be allowed to become a
fixation, and I should suggest that the subject should not " go after "
the habit, like a savage watchdog, but should deal with himself like
a gentle father, and call himself to order with a smile whenever
needful. But he must be patient, for persistence will prevail in the
end. It should not be forgotten, too, that with the dreaming habit
as with others, it is more a case of directing the mind to what is
positive rather than purely negative. For example, one who is able
to understand the meaning of the Rosary can make this the alter-
native positive subject of his mind, and this will be of value even if
the devotion is of no great intensity. Another may prefer to dwell
upon recollections of a pleasing nature drawn from his past life, or he
may think of plans for future activities. In any case, the mind is
distracted and turns to fruitful channels.

The day-dreaming of this type of character is very similar to the
brooding self-absorption of the obsessional type. The difference is
chiefly outward. The dreamer dwells mainly upon images associated with pleasure, the brooder upon fears and anxieties. In both
cases, there is no positive goal ; real thought, on the other hand,
leads to increased knowledge and actual decision. Brooding and
day-dreaming are a species of abuse of the natural power of thought.
Mental hygiene is an education directed towards concrete thought
and decision ; it does not permit of a meaningless, sterile playing
with the power of thought.

The sexual neurotic, who is very often also an onanist, finds the obsessional thoughts which press upon him to be heavy burdens. They are apt to revolve about ideas which he feels to be sinful and a cause of fear. We often meet with the type who thinks dangerous thoughts can be banished with a shake of the head and a firm "No !" Such thoughts retreat for a short time and then they return. This kind of fearful repudiation of the thoughts arising in the mind—even when aided by prayer—is apt to render the subject still more vulnerable ; for the sexual elements disappear only to bury themselves in the subconscious ; and being merely suppressed and not dealt with along positive lines, they lie in wait to make themselves felt again.

Accordingly, in such a case it is necessary to attack the unsolved problem ; the subject must ask himself questions and answer them, perhaps with the aid of someone possessing expert knowledge. By doing so he will bring about a harmonious relationship between the higher centres of personality and the sex instinct, for this is the only real method of overcoming his difficulties. If the imaginary world in which the thoughts wander is peopled with pleasurable ideas, it will be of little use to look for aid to empty and bloodless images, calculated to give rise to monotony rather than real distraction. The material with which the mind is occupied must be beautiful and filled with strength and true experience ; it must be calculated to fill the young spirit with fire and enthusiasm. This kind of concrete help is essential to the young. It is not enough to say: "You must distract your mind." It will be well to go through the suggested lines of thought with him, preparing the ground and making useful suggestions.

The following is a useful piece of advice. When you find yourself beset by undesirable images, change your surroundings. If alone and lonely, seek society and openings for talk and discussion. If you are lying in bed, get up or begin to read an absorbing book or concentrate upon putting the mind out of action through systematic relaxation. If idle, turn to some interesting form of activity. All these things must be done without nervous tension in a completely natural and quiet manner. This applies also to prayer.

Love and Morality

Finally, let me say that I look upon morality as the science of values *sub specie aeternitatis* ; as they must be viewed in the light of eternity. Our moral life rests upon a courageous venturing of our whole life, with all its powers, in the cause of that which we know to be good and right. The object of education and self-education is to produce a character with the courage to make independent decisions

and to translate them into the actions that his conscience tells him
represent ultimate values. Purity is a splendid thing, but it is not
the ultimate or even the really decisive value. Gügler points out that
it is detrimental to the work of education if we take our stand upon
the principle that sexual purity is equivalent to purity as such, and
that chastity is the highest virtue and the cornerstone of morality.
This is an error almost as dangerous as that other mistaken idea
that he who does not offend against the law and the commandments
is righteous and justified. It is not enough to observe the law—we
have *to fulfil it*. The law does not exist for its own sake. *Love is the
foundation.* It is love that is demanded of us, and through love alone
can we truly fulfil the moral law.

APPENDIX

The following contributions appeared for the first time in the *Katechetische Blätter*, published by Kösel-Verlag (Munich and Kempten). The dates of publication are to be found at the foot of each contribution. (*Tr. Note*)

MORAL AND THEOLOGICAL NOTES ON THE PROBLEM OF SELF-ABUSE

by RUPERT ANGERMAIR
Professor of Moral Theology, Freising

MORAL THEOLOGY concerns itself, in the first place, with the essential nature of the virtue or sin under consideration in order to understand the object ; in the second place, with the subjective attitude with a view to judging the actual moral quality of specific acts ; and thirdly, with the deeper causes with the view of giving help in the care of souls.

1—Self-Abuse as a Sin

It was formerly held that the essential sinfulness of this habit lay in the fact that the seed intended rightly for propagation was voluntarily wasted. Apart altogether from the natural impossibility of so many millions of seeds coming to fruition, this argument must lead to the view that self-abuse cannot be sinful if performed by children too young to be capable of propagation or by old people past the age when it is possible. In reality, however, such quasi-onanistic practices by children approaching puberty as well as by the elderly are felt naturally to be shameful and sins giving offence to God. Nor can we look for a satisfying reason in the supposed sinfulness of sexual pleasure as such ; for in that case manipulations of this kind carried out, not in order to obtain pleasure, but purely as a measure of relief would not carry with them the sense of depression which they actually do. The deepest causes of moral judgment are not to be sought so much in the later consequences of an act as in the essential nature of the act itself, which precedes the consequences.

Applying this principle to self-abuse, we realise that the primary factor lies in the confusion introduced into the divine order ; in the denial of man's essential nature in its individual, social, and universal aspects. On the *individual* side, sexual power is an attribute of human nature and is bound up with personal love and all its effects. In the case of self-abuse, however, it is clear that the sexual urge is isolated from all its personal and human associations and responsibilities and made into a means of pleasure alone. Here the personality, which should rule over " nature," becomes subordinate to the crude impersonal urge of the flesh ; the higher *ego* is placed below the *id* of the lower centres. This signifies a disturbance and lowering of the personality as a whole.

On the *social* side, we must remember that man is essentially a social being and cannot fail to feel that practices of an onanistic type are a betrayal of the normal sex relationship to another human being, with all the social consequences normally attached to sexual life. This a-social attitude is expressed very clearly in the marked fear of disgrace which is automatically associated with the habit ; for the victim is conscious that he is not a healthy member of the community and not serving it with his whole nature. The very names " secret sin " and " solitary sin ", popularly attached to the practice, express the feeling that it is of an a-social nature.

As to the *universal and religious* aspect of the problem, it will be noted that, considered fundamentally, it is the all-wise and omnipotent God Who created sexual power, with its individual and social significance, and thus it is natural that any confusion introduced into this plan is a disobedient act.

Our faith in the triune God indwelling in us by grace and in our body as the temple of the Holy Ghost can only deepen our feeling of the offence against God that is involved, of necessity, in this abuse of sexual power.

In the following remarks we shall speak more of *helping* sufferers from this habit than of its condemnation ; but this must by no means be held to signify that we adopt any lax attitude towards this widespread evil.

We are dealing with a human error that is, objectively speaking, extremely regrettable.

2—The Subjective Judgment of Self-Abuse

How far, having accepted the above view, we may regard each specific act as a sin, or a mortal sin, will depend upon the subjective conditions determining it : how far actual knowledge was present and how free was the will. In this connection it must be said that knowledge and will are more easily and more seriously diminished and weakened in the case of a sin of this sort—which is so bound up with the emotions and so immediately linked to the confused life of the senses— than with many others sins, such as the neglect of religious duties or of duty to love the neighbour. The Creator, it is true, gave us as a means of protecting our purity not only rational knowledge but a deeply rooted sense of shame, in as far as this concerns itself with sex. However, in most of the cases met with in the care of souls, we find habits that have been established for a lengthy period which have either considerably weakened the sense of shame or, precisely on account of the inward shame they cause, impel again and again towards further attempts to employ the habit as a means of deadening the inward self. Moreover, the beginnings of quasi-onanistic practices often take place at a time when sexual maturity is not yet attained and the adolescent does not fully understand himself or his sense of shame. There often results in this fashion a quite natural habit (*consuetudo naturalis*) at a time when the subject has not sufficient knowledge of himself to be able to take up the right attitude. This habit penetrates to the roots of the soul-body relationship and establishes a kind of psychophysical pattern. When, at a later date, the meaning of the action becomes clearer, a certain discrepancy between the strength of the instinctive urge and the power of the will is already an established fact. Even after the most earnest attempts at betterment, set-backs may (not *must!*) occur, which seem to be due more or less to a physical compulsion, the will being by no means necessarily bad but of inadequate strength.

Many decisions of a moral nature may already have been made in a premature sense and have created bad habits ; these cannot be overlooked when we come to deal with the case as a whole. For the time being we can reckon as truly " sinful " only that which stems from a retraction, in whole or in part, of the will to amend. If the set-backs become increasingly rare, that may be taken as a sign that the will to overcome can be lasting and effective. The physical act does not give rise to " sin," nor does a will that is innocent, but too weak ; but only a *bad* will and the free personal decision to do wrong. One cannot climb out of a bog with a single stride. But a case in which the penitent, although backsliding to a certain extent, has honestly endeavoured to follow the path leading out of the bog but has not had sufficient strength fully to succeed, should be judged in quite a different fashion from the case of another penitent, with the same degree of backsliding, who, if honest, must admit that he freely and consciously kept to the path leading down into the bog.

Those, too, have a right to be judged mildly who began this bad habit consciously and with consent of the will (*conseutudo moralis*) but then firmly resolved to make an end of it, once and for all. They cannot, perhaps, with wills already weakened, secure swift victory over sensual urges which have established a foothold, even with their best efforts. When, in such cases, it seems clear that the path leads out of the bog one should be careful not to discourage them. In dealing with strange penitents, it is well to ask questions to find out the general moral trend: what was the position at the last confessions ? is the present position an improvement or not?

In specific cases, full consciousness and relatively free will is not readily to be assumed if the actual act occurs suddenly, following upon a lengthy period of indecision, when the subject is pulled this way and that by desire and resistance, and, looking back, cannot recollect a precise moment of consent. The penitent who acted with full consent will usually be aware of the fact. In other cases, it is perhaps more the *id*, the lower urges below the level of consicousness, which has swept the penitent away, than the real self, acting as a free agent of consent. If he has the impression that he did not " come to himself " until after the act, we can assume that beforehand he was not fully himself—at any rate not in the " existential depth " of his true ego. In the same fashion, we may doubt the presence of adequate consciousness and free will in cases of a morbid depression of mind and spirit and of strong emotional excitement (not self-induced), or where we have a partially conscious state, as when half asleep. Similar reasoning may be applied to the penitent who normally regards a grave sin with horror and at once returns to his normal attitude in case of being overtaken by a sudden set-back and is able to say that he would never have fallen had he been in full possession of himself ; one who is sincerely struggling to find the right path may well argue thus. The sin of self-abuse, it must not be forgotten, invades the personality as a whole ; and while bearing the foregoing in mind we must not forget that persons given to the practice are more inclined in many cases than are other sinners to bring forward somewhat weak excuses for their actions.

Above all, the priest must not forget that, even if the subjective character of particular cases may be judged mildly, the attitude of the onanist in general must be looked upon as highly regrettable. For this reason the priest must never regard his task as finished when he has passed judgment upon the sins of the past: he is the shepherd of souls and his function as judge must be supplemented by the giving of responsible aid for the future.

3—Spiritual Aid

The problem of giving aid to the victims of this habit should be considered in relation to the objective causes and subjective motives lying behind the habit itself. These causes may be more causal or more purposeful in their nature. As a rule both factors are mingled.

The penitent who takes up the habit for the sake of the pleasure received, whose actions are *purposeful*, is clearly the true sinner. He can be saved only by a thoroughgoing religious and moral renewal, a complete reorientation. His whole thought and feeling and all his values must be wrong. The value of purity must be brought home to him with so much force and sympathy that he will shrink from no sacrifice in order consciously to place the higher values, both natural and supernatural, above the lower value of isolated sense pleasure, even if this costs him sacrifice and heroic effort. However important the supernatural values may be for those who are capable of grasping them, even in their case the natural values must receive their due position in the hierarchy of the personality. Otherwise, the life of grace cannot build as it should upon the life of nature. It may often prove a great help to a young boy or girl whose general attitude is such that he can receive this truth, if one can make clear to him the full value of a noble personal love, capable, even at this early age, of bestowing happiness and of leading later to a real and blessed married union. To take human feeling as a starting point, one may seek to show that purity is not a deprivation of love but the highest quality of true love and that it alone can bring out the personal values of self and partner. Sexual desire by itself reduces the supposedly loved one to the level of a mere means for the gratification of one's own " needs "—a horrible notion !

In those cases where onanism can be traced back to a previous incapacity for real love, a cure can often be brought about quite speedily, if the subject is able to find a good and pure girl to whom he is moved to render homage— perhaps only from a distance—or to love with youth's romantic idealistic love.

He will not wish to desecrate the object of his dreams with impure thoughts or wishes. Satisfaction of the heart on the ideal plane not infrequently leads to the subject's actually *forgetting* sex on the plane of physical satisfaction.

The idea of damming up the bodily and spiritual forces and turning them into constructive channels for upbuilding the whole personality can often exert a powerful influence over the young mind. Lack of self-control will then be felt as damaging to the whole personality, as signifying a loss of self-respect and personal freedom. But if the personality is in a state of disintegration, the path to personal love and a right relationship to a worthy partner is endangered. These immanent aims and motives should be related to the good will of God the Father who wishes to make his children happy and sanctions purity with supernatural motives and also with threats and punishments. Thus presented, the problem is no longer one of frightening the subject—a method usually more destructive than constructive with sufferers from self-abuse, for when thrust into a state of despair they turn again and again to the self-satisfaction found in their practices.

Those for whom marriage does not enter into the question (think of the excess of women over men!) should be directed towards thinking of the value of purity in itself and its relationship with love in the wider sense, together with the social service that can be given to the community by those having purity and good will. The lonely " Auntie," for example, should not forget that she may have a wide field of usefulness amongst her relations and her neighbours ; and that important tasks within the parish may have been allotted to her by providence. Beyond all these things, the last and highest value of purity is revealed in a wholehearted and loving devotion to Christ Himself.

To a very large extent the practice of self-abuse is more casual than purposeful in its origins. It is not simply the desire for pleasure that impels the penitent in this direction ; it is the impulse to escape from something else that presses upon him. This is especially the case with self-abuse amongst children. These causal factors do not exclude an evil will or an indifferent attitude, at a later date, but they cannot be removed or ignored purely through the will ; the latter may be strengthened and purified, but the causes in the background must be attacked at the same time.

It is important to make it clear that not every neurosis is rooted in sexual habits ; many sexual abberrations arise from an already existent neurosis. Father and mother complexes, amongst other factors, even in very early years, can reveal that a marriage—quite unconsciously perhaps—is far from suitable for the children. As the child grows older and approaches maturity, he will take no interest in preserving his powers for a future marriage and is more likely to " try out " temptations for himself. It is possible, too, that problems of physical growth and disturbances in assimilation (such as may result from a sudden liberation after long imprisonment) may disturb the functions of the glands and the hormonic system: neurotic erections may then result, quite of their own accord : a state of affairs leading easily to self-abuse, even in the absence (at least at first) of sexual aims and purposes. The psychophysical tensions create an automatic urge to relieve tension. If the parents or doctors know of any kind of organic inferiority likely to deter the subject either consciously (or, at an earlier age, unconsciously) from a later normal married life and thus to encourage substitute actions, the educator and the priest should insist that everything possible should be done to eliminate physical conditions tending towards self-abuse. It may be only a *phimosis*, a slight contraction of the foreskin, which can affect the sebaceous matter of the skin, causing inflammation and some irritation ; it may also hinder spontaneous nocturnal pollutions, creating another factor making for self-abuse. A very simple operation is usually enough to remove a trouble which must give rise to some difficulties in marriage at a later date.

In cases where the subject of self-abuse does not show marked signs of a perversion of values, anthropological, social or religious, the priest confessor or the educator must draw attention to the possibility of casual factors in the habit. This will strengthen his position as an understanding friend, and help to secure the necessary confidence. Such an explanation will be of much value to the subject in reducing his feeling of inferiority, and in encouraging him to go forward more hopefully, while doing his best, free from anxiety, to establish natural conditions helping him to get rid of his troublesome urges. Undesirable pressure of the sexual urge can often be avoided by physical exercise and hardening ; but excessive fatigue is best avoided. There should be no overindulgence in flesh foods, alcohol, or nicotine. Every sort of softening and spoiling, whether by self or through others, is also to be avoided. Interesting mental occupation that satisfies but does not unduly excite will help to distract the mind from sexual phantasies.

It would be most unwise to make light of the sinfulness of these practices, when carried out with consent of the will—as is the case with no small percentage of the subjects—yet at the same time we must draw attention to a further possibility which cannot be overlooked in an age when degeneracy is widespread. In those cases where the methods above outlined, in spite of genuine good will, do not lead to liberation it often becomes necessary, for the time being, to bring *comfort* to the sinner, rather than to cause him too much fear and anxiety. Excessive growth can result from over-activity of the glands controlling growth, and a certain proportion of young people may suffer from a somewhat similar over-activity of the sexual glands, constituting a burden which cannot speedily be mastered, even given a will that is sincere, or even heroic. The right balance between powerful urges and a strong will may take some time to establish and the conditions cannot be accurately foreseen.

If the priest or educator has good reason to believe that the penitent is of good will and sincerely wishes for betterment, despite the discrepancy between his bodily and spiritual powers, he should do his best to educate him in a knowledge of himself, to face the situation honestly. He should learn to distinguish between genuine sinfulness and guilt and deplorable weakness. In a severe case, if the priest or educator is firmly convinced of the situation above described, he may urge the penitent not to stay away from Communion—always provided, needless to say, that after sincere self-examination he feels sure that his will is actively and sincerely turned in the right direction. If his personal relationship to God is cultivated with special care, it is perhaps possible for him to be liberated sooner than would be likely otherwise. In his prayers let him not confuse grace with miracles ; and he must not demand or expect some miraculous change in his difficult constitution. The grace of God will be sufficient to protect him, at least, from committing any subjective grave sin. The body alone does not sin, nor does phantasy, as long as it urges itself upon the subject without his will and is not nourished ; the free will alone can sin. Such reading as *Introduction to the Devout Life* by Francis de Sales (IV, 3, 4, 5) will help to strengthen his will and increase his confidence in the righteousness of God.

So much for the causes and motives of self-abuse, in their relation to moral judgment. Where it would seem that the young person in question continues this practice for the sake of pleasure, after beginning in childhood or later from causal reasons, causal therapy must work hand in hand with a re-education in values and healing aid be associated with the proper degree of severity. A too mild judgment of an evil so deeply regrettable from the objective standpoint cannot be of aid to anyone ; the priest must not give up his position as exhorter and confessor to become a *mere* psychotherapist. If we have given up the old-fashioned terroristic pedagogy in this matter in favour of a policy of encouragement, it is not because we no longer take sin seriously ; it is because we seldom know, with precision, what are the ultimate deepest reasons for this particular sin and, even if an evil or careless will is responsible, we believe ourselves able to render greater service to the penitent by way of the goodness of the Good Shepherd than would be possible by means of the repentance and hell-fire approach, either by itself or at the wrong time and with the wrong person.

(*September*, 1950)

PHENOMENOLOGY AND PSYCHOPATHOLOGY OF SELF-ABUSE

by Baron V. E. von Gebsattel

IN THE PSYCHOPATHOLOGY of the present day there are only two modes of research that take it upon themselves to explain the aberrations of sexual life by means of a single theory: the psychoanalytical and the anthropological. The former is represented by Freud and his school, the latter by H. Kunz, E. Strauss and von Gebsattel. The psychoanalytical theory is an offspring of the natural-istic-positivistic school of medicine and carries its methods over into the " organism of the mind," interpreting this as a dynamic play of forces. It builds up a theory of perversions, seeing these as false developments of the sexual impulse.

This doctrine of perversions certainly appears to form a logical unified picture ; nevertheless it breaks down, owing to a neglect of personality and the structure of the perverse type of being underlying the psychopathic phenomena. This can never be fully understood if the sexual man is oversimplified by reducing him, after the causal genetic methods, to a bundle of instincts which, in their turn, are reshuffled in a mechanical fashion to explain the relevant disturbances of sexual life as witnessed in medical experience. The anthropol-ogical theory of perversion, on the other hand, takes its bearings from the sexual structure of personal being. It starts with the idea that every sexual aberration derives its force from the destruction of a normal sexual reality, so that the real *meaning* of the perverse phenomenon is to be perceived in the " de-formation " of this normal sex life.

As to self-abuse in the literature of to-day, it is debated whether it should be regarded as a " fragmentary perversion " (Kunz), a " primeval perversion " (Hattingberg), or as a " mere technique for the production of a sexual orgasm " (M. Boss), in which case it would not rank as a perversion. The observation that the habit can serve modes of experience that are normal as well as those that are perverse seems to strengthen the view of M. Boss. One thing is certain: in the problem of onanism it is not the *act* of self-abuse, as such, that is decisive but the place it occupies in the development and structure of the individual. The psychiatrist speaks of the *psychopathia sexualis*, the psychoanalyst of a sexual urge and of the genesis of " sexual aberrations," including self-abuse ; but the doctor who thinks along anthropological lines must always bear in mind that these are scientific abstractions detached from reality, which consists of living *individuals* with their own sexual lives, in which they either give expression to values based upon love, or live by their rejection of these values.

It is certainly the case that one calls perverse a type of behaviour which, in its actual completion, does not fit into the pattern inherent in the logic of the natural order itself. If the psychiatric diagnostic means by " perversion " an alteration in the lasting nature of the sex life, the occurrence of self-abuse in the case of an individual at certain times will not necessarily amount to a perversion ; the point can be considered only in relation to the whole person-ality. Onanism may represent a change in the life-pattern. The psychiatrist speaks of onanism as he might refer to fetishism or masochism. That is to say that one can have personalities which exhibit, in their sexual lives, a kind of compulsory addiction such as is characteristic of all true perversions, in the field of self-abuse. In this special sense we may speak of self-abuse as a per-version ; but it must distinguish itself from other forms of the habit to be so described, for, in the clinical sense, self-abuse is not to be classed as necessarily a perversion.

Considerations of this sort are to be found, often unconsciously, behind attempts to describe the various possibilities which determine self-abuse. If onanism, in the strict sense of the term—as an established addiction—is to be regarded as a serious departure from the normal, one cannot say the same about the very widespread practice of self-abuse amongst the young which is more a psychiatric problem than one brought before doctors under the head of *adiaphoron*. The same may be said about the so-called " self-abuse from necessity" of those condemned to sexual abstinence. From the standpoint of psychiatry, the two types (" self-abuse from necessity " and onanism) represent the two extremes in the scale of values applying to sexual manifestations, the former being psychopathic in the lowest degree and the latter in the highest. In between the two extremes we may note innumerable variations demanding specific consideration. The so-called self-abuse of a small child may be looked upon as a " border-line " case : for, whether accompanied by feelings of pleasure or not, it is more a kind of playful manipulation of the genital organs that else, and has not, as yet, the character of a truly libidinous sexual act. We cannot actually speak of the latter until such time as the growing child has achieved a measure of separation from its body ; this begins to set in when the child masters its own excretions, when it is "house trained ", and the mind takes control of the rhythm of bodily processes. The child then reaches a stage when it feels itself separated from the unconscious acts of the body. Now we can speak of the *urge* to urinate and pass movements, and of the mastery of this urge. At the same time the child can experience an oscillation of the vital impulse between the urge and its control through the mind, with states of tension giving rise to a libidinous interest in the region of the excretions. This tends to support the Freudian conception of the " anal masturbation " of the small child. Here we may perceive the pre-sexual roots of later self-abuse.

In order to clarify the various types of self-abuse, we recommend the following arrangement :

1. The playful actions of small children in playing with their genital organs ; this is no true self-abuse and is often a substitute for nose-picking, sucking, or " anal boring."

2. Self-abuse in early puberty as a preliminary stage of erotic life with a partner. The pseudo self-abuse of the very early years continues, sometimes without a break and sometimes after an interval, into the stage of the self-abuse of early puberty. But, even in the absence of this introductory stage, one sees from about eleven years on (usually somewhat later) a pre-occupation with the genital organs. In the case of girls this may be started by the sensations of pleasure experienced in washing the parts in question, and with boys by the beginning of erections. In the early years of puberty, one can witness both girls and boys practising self-abuse with—so to say—a " good conscience "; that is, without any feeling of guilt.* A different outlook does not result, as might be thought, solely through outward influence (such as the warnings of educators) but often *spontaneously* when a certain age is reached and the conscience, for reasons which cannot be exactly defined, begins to be active of its own accord. In other cases, the conscience becomes active when the ejaculation takes place for the first time—although not at once in a fully conscious manner. What we often hear from boys is that first they feel disturbed by ineasiness in the genital places and try to quiet this with various manipulations, but, when an ejaculation suddenly takes place outside control, they feel a sense of shame and tend to regard it as sort of bed-wetting.

The further development of self-abuse is often largely dominated by the conflict with conscience. With respect to self-abuse during puberty we may remark that this does not, as a rule, come within the scope of the psychiatrist but is a matter for the house doctor and above all for the priest. It is often the case that an explanatory talk about sexual life has surprisingly good results with those whose urge to practise self-abuse is inflamed by anxiety and fear. It is a matter of experience that the most effective method of relieving the youthful urge towards self-abuse is not by a direct attack but by the encouragement of

*It is to be noted that a feeling of resistance to the habit of self-abuse can arise as a *preliminary form* of conscience when, to the hitherto accepted practice, is added a consciousness of the adult attitude, as is seen, for example, when a child thinks : " I might have been seen doing it ! " It is thus a matter of experience that children who go to confession are inclined to criticise themselves for the habit earlier than those who do not.

friendships and comradely associations with others of the same age, of either sex.
One sometimes finds that the urge towards self-abuse will gradually vanish under
the influence of innocent relationships of this kind. Or it may disappear spontaneously without any special method of dealing with it and without sexual
intercourse, even after self-abuse has been practised for years without any visible
injury, just as if the course of development had brought the subject beyond it and
the desire died away ; or again the habit may take on the vehement urge more
proper to puberty, and be felt, subjectively, as a compulsion. In these cases the
aid of a doctor should be sought. One can often observe in such cases that what
has taken place is a "sexualisation of a lasting conflict" with the subject's
environment (school or home). When the conflict is tackled it usually leads to a
considerable relief of the urge. But side-by-side with this, it is often needful to
solve a " sexualised inhibition of the conscience " and with the help of the subject
himself, to undertake re-education and the building up of positive aims. We
should point out that the latent psychophysical sexual tension of young people
in the stage of puberty can, at times, be manifested as states of anxiety of an
unfathomable kind.

3.   The so-called " self-abuse from necessity." This description might be
applied to the conditions often obtaining in puberty and adolescence. But,
strictly speaking, the term is used in relation to adults who are deprived of a
sexual partner, for one reason or another ; for example, when the marriage
partner does not function as such, or through separation (as with sailors, soldiers,
etc.). In such cases, the subject often feels a justification for his abnormal conduct.
This type of self-abuse is often associated with a special " sexual constitution,"
in which the urge to detumescence is peculiarly urgent and imperious. When
these cases come under the observation of a doctor he must ask himself such
questions as these: Does the regression to self-abuse, in the case of marriage
conflict, contain an element of *revenge* ?   does the asserted irresistible urgency
not represent, in the last analysis, no more than a special case of lack of self-
control? Those who feel compelled to resort to this habit often assert that,
without it, they are hindered seriously in their work and cannot recover their
capacity until relief has been found.

4.   There are forms of self-abuse which are, in a special sense, symptoms of a
disturbance of the normal dual-relationship of the sexes. Thus we see the habit
manifested in association with perverse tendencies, all of which may be regarded
as deformations of normal sexual love : e.g., fetichists, voyeurs, exhibitionists,
are always at the same time onanists. Regarded quite strictly, even when it
comes to sexual intercourse—as in sado-masochism, Don Juanism, or homosexuality—this *still* has the character of auto-eroticism, of a species of disguised
self-abuse, because the sex impulse does not serve the purpose of a genuine
bi-personal love union.
In connection with the dependence of self-abuse upon perverse tendencies,
we must not forget the exaggerated love of self, the " narcissism " referred to by
Freud. This is characterised, not only by the basic factor—a destruction
of the organic union between the subject and his fellow-men, but, further, by that
peculiar *splitting* of the developing human being within himself, which is in
accordance with his half-developed spiritual personality. There is an inter-
mediate phase lying in between the naïve discovery of his own body by the young
child, and the self-discovery of later years—a phase characterised by an urge on
the part of the adolescent youth (originating in his sexual ripening) to re-unite
himself with his own bodily life from which, at an earlier stage, when approaching maturity, he had felt himself becoming separated. Not yet has it become
clear that this love union with the bodily self can take place only as a by-product
of bodily union with a partner of the opposite sex (see Novalis, Fragmt. 1950).
Thus, in this phase of self-love, it often comes to an onanistic pseudo-union with
the bodily self (love of one's own reflection). The deplorable consequences
which follow upon acts of self-abuse inflamed by this kind of love, prove that the
splitting of the self which motivates them is not cured in this way, but, on the
contrary, is more firmly established.

This brings us to the destructive aspect of self-abuse as rooted in the nature of the body itself. Thus considered, it may be seen as a hindrance to the formation of a *physical unity* expressing the sexual polarity of the subject. For in every act of self-abuse there is inherent the division of this basic unity, since the consciousness directing the act itself cannot fulfil its purpose, without operating upon the sexual pole of the physical body, so that a division is essential to the nature of the act. It is thus regressive, since it hinders the formative unifying intention of genuine love.

The apparent satisfaction of self-abuse must be accompanied by an element of dissatisfaction, and this is the deeper reason why self-abuse may become so rooted as to develop into established onanism, a real *addiction*. After each act, there remains a certain degree of dissatisfaction ; this impels towards further acts which in their turn fail to satisfy, and so on, leading to an ever-increasing addiction. The same element of dissatisfaction followed by self-abuse is to be observed in the case of sexual unions between persons of opposite sexes and in married life, when a latent opposition to the partner robs the union of its true character of fulfilment. Such an oppositional attitude can often be traced back to a strong tie (positive or negative) with a mother, sister, father or brother. The dissolution of such a tie by psychoanalysis is the only effective means of dealing with the type of self-abuse arising from this situation, sometimes referred to as " deferred self-abuse ; " for it may go on for one reason or another into the sixties and seventies. Sometimes in conjunction with the frigidity or impotence of a partner there may be a recurrence of this so-called " matrimonial onanism," the treatment of which will also remove a similar tendency on the part of the partner.

Again we may find forms of onanism which are based upon hatred of the body and its needs and these cannot be understood unless we realise that a strong anger gives them the character of attempts to *destroy* sexual life. Or, yet again, there are forms rooted in feelings of depression and emptiness from which a reaction to self-abuse may give a false appearance of relief.

Sometimes—and not so very seldom—we note, particularly with celibates, sudden relapses into self-abuse occurring periodically when an individual, male or female, meets with a demand or claim involving a fuller realisation of their own personalities, and then for one reason or another—perhaps outward pressure or perhaps inward fears, laziness, or mere indecision—the opportunity thus offered is not accepted and the realisation fails to take place.

In the foregoing we have taken up no more than a small selection of the innumerable possibilities open to us. Let us, above all, not forget that the really *fundamental method* to be adopted by the doctor in fighting against onanism consists in directing the penitent, or patient, *positively* towards the dual life-mode of our human existence, primarily realised through marriage.

(*October*, 1950)

SELF-ABUSE AS A SYMPTOM

by FREDERICK VON GAGERN

IT FREQUENTLY HAPPENS that priests and doctors find themselves faced with patients who have come to consult them specifically on the matter of self-abuse. This seems to them the basic evil and one hears it said : " If it were not for this habit, everything would be all right ! "

The doctor or the priest will often agree with the view that self-abuse, either as disease or sin, occupies a place of its own, like a cancerous growth in medicine, or an act of adultery in the confessional. They incline, accordingly, to attack the disease or the " vice " (as the case may be) with all sorts of medical, pedagogical, or spiritual weapons. The following will make it clear that this approach to the problem is often an error ; at the same time, we shall see what practical depth psychology has to tell us about the nature of self-abuse.

The ten-year-old Hans was brought before the doctor by his mother :
she pointed out to his stained knickers as evidence of the " crime," saying :
" That is the sort of boy I have ! " The little fellow was totally abashed at this
demonstration of his " depravity " in the presence of the mother. The doctor
spoke at first with him alone. He gave full vent to his despair : " I have tried
everything ; my whole effort is directed towards overcoming this vice. Again
and again I go to confession and take Communion. A priest advised me to
go for walks or to take up reading. I have done these things and many more in
order to break away from self-abuse (notice the concentration upon the habit)
but nothing does any good. Nothing can save me now, and I shall certainly
go to Hell ! "

1—The Vain Struggle

Most priests have already discovered that a concentrated effort to overcome
this habit is usually futile. In the majority of cases—especially when we are
dealing with onanism (that is to say, an excessive urge and addiction to self-abuse)
—it is as if the victim's habit grew stronger the more he struggled, after the
pattern of the confessional instruction, to overcome the fault. " The more I
pray about it, the more it overwhelms me ! " " I have noticed that I practise
the habit more the more I seek to overcome it." How often do we not hear
such sayings as these ? Why must this be so ? Are we not compelled to think
of an abscess beneath a tooth, for example, when no pain-destroying medicine
can be of any real use because it deals merely with *symptoms* ? To turn the mind
towards the habit seems to increase its power. The more energy is used up in
this sort of struggle, the less remains for the patient's fight for spiritual development.

2—Distraction *from*—not struggle *against!*

The great thing is to take the mind of the victim of self-abuse away from
his habit and to avoid everything that can remind him of it. In the case of the
boy mentioned above, the priest recommended physical and mental activity.
This is quite right in itself. It becomes clear, however, that our little Hans was
so much in the grip of his complex with respect to his supposed mortal sin, that
this well-meaned distraction was not successful. It was thus necessary first of all
to ease his sensation of guilt. In the care of souls this can often be done with
some success. The customary question, " Did you like doing this? " and the
answer spontaneously given by most penitents, " Oh no ! I struggle so hard
against it," demonstrate a process of an " unconsciously compulsory character,"
which does not depend on free will. The visible limitation of free will in this
urge to abuse can, accordingly, allow the priest to comfort the penitent by
explaining that, in this case, there is no possible question of a " mortal sin "
and it must not be taken more tragically than any other venial fault.

The way is thus opened to a more positive outlook : the attention of the
penitent can be turned to other aspects of life. In the case of this little boy it
transpired that his school work was backward, that he was not a good comrade
at school and that he tended to withdraw into himself when at home. In
conversation it was possible to discuss these problems with the view of turning
the energies of the boy towards improvement in these fields. Working together
with the doctor, the boy sought to discover how he could utilise his efforts in a
positive manner.

3—Satisfaction

Above and beyond all this it must not be forgotten that self-abuse is not
incorrectly described in German as *Selbst-befriedigung* (self-satisfaction) because
it does afford a satisfaction, although a merely apparent and mistaken one, in
the absence of real sex satisfaction.

A student of theology told me that as long as he was working at his college
he had no trouble as regards self-abuse. But in the holidays the habit always
overcame him. At home he felt that he was out of place : as a future pastor he

did not take part in the work of the farm (why not?) and the girls of the place kept away from him because he was a student of theology ; in short he was made to feel superfluous. Here we see the function of self-abuse as a kind of compensation and a symptom of a false attitude towards work and society. When this wrong attitude was corrected the symptomatic self-abuse disappeared of itself.

4—Moral and Spiritual Causes

In the case of the little Hans, the reasons for his spiritual trouble came out in conversation. The manner in which his mother dragged him before the doctor, like a policeman bringing a prisoner to the magistrate, was an indication in itself of a wrong attitude, of a lack of love and warmth, and of any attempt to understand the little fellow's troubles. The boy himself complained that his mother was very strict and never gave him any tenderness. When he turned to her for warmth and security, he was usually bruskly rejected. She never had any time for him if he wanted to ask her questions of an awkward nature ; or she might even scold him for his natural curiosity. He had become more and more alienated from his mother. He has lost confidence and felt desperately lonely. His father was lost during the war. His sleep was often disturbed, and he had a lot anxiety dreams, when he was sometimes bitten by a snake, or a dragon sought to devour him.

There was thus a close connection between the lack of maternal affection and the lack of satisfaction in the child's life. The warmth and security of the mother is the life of the child. Love and vital encouragement are necessities for the child, and it seeks them in every way, conscious and unconscious. They are the springs of its life. Should they be denied or be given inadequately, there may be an adjustment outwardly and in the conscious mind ; but, deep down in the subconscious, the personality will unceasingly pursue them and yearn after them. This is one of the commonest sources of spiritual maladjustment and of symptomatic self-abuse. Even the adult who has experienced this sort of trouble and need will continue, basically, to seek after the warmth and security which, as child, he did not receive. We must not, however, forget that the causes thus described do not apply equally to all the victims of self-abuse. There are other backgrounds that may be responsible. In the case of Hans the explanation given is completely adequate.

5—Treatment

The result of the investigation of the case of Hans is an indication of the right method of treatment, which can be summarised as follows:

(a) The necessary liberation from the cramping sense of guilt, with the consequent possibility of distraction from the habit itself ;

(b) The exploration of the background of the trouble and the provision of new positive aims ;

(c) Psychotherapeutic treatment of the mother.

Attention has been drawn to the first point (a) in section 1 of this article. The theologian knows of the diasatrous consequences of the *fascinositas negocitatis* in which a man does not attain to a positive expression of his moral and spiritual forces, because he is hindered by the lack of opportunity in his environment. The doctor, or other helper, must construct a bridge for the patient, across which his good positive energies can move in order to reach real life. In the first place, the onanist is inclined to look upon himself as separated from normal persons by his " depravity." He finds himself in a state of more or less marked isolation, his attention becomes fixed upon himself and he loses interest in his fellow men. The mere fact of knowing that the habit of self-abuse is extremely common, —so much so that some ninety per cent of all persons have practised it at one time or another—will come as great relief to him; he will no longer feel himself singled out as an exceptionally depraved character, and the way to participate in the life of his fellow men will be more open.

The path towards God will be smoothed when the onanist is no longer burdened with so heavy a sense of supposed guilt. We find priests who will tell the penitent that, in his case, the habit is not a sin ; it is a disease. Here is a difficulty: even when a penitent is told that he has not committed a sin, he does not for that reason lose his feeling of guilt. How does this come about? There are two reasons: first there is the customary " training " casting suspicion upon everything to do with sex, so that his action results, automatically, in sensations of guilt. We all know this type of rigid training, which is often so lamentably successful in the sexual field that, in not a few cases, it proves able to poison the whole married life of the subject. The second reason may be found in a *real* feeling of guilt in the conscience, as distinct from the unreal, as above. Here the feeling of guilt does *not* concern the self-abuse but goes deeper, *down to the causes in the background,* of which the habit, as we know, is but a *symptom,* the outward characteristic of some inward fault in the life attitude : " I cannot help feeling in my innermost self, that something in my attitude towards the tasks imposed upon me by God, is not as it ought to be." This becomes evident to the conscious mind more especially when it takes the form of an " outward sign." Just as fever, sickness, and pain are symptoms of an inflammation of the appendix although they do not constitute the illness itself, so the " sinful " action is a symptom of an alienation from God, in the form of some *wrong attitude* towards the life given by God. The sin is not confined to the act. Thus the feeling of sin persists after the penitent has been told (and realises) that the symptom is not sinful.

The patient must learn to understand this : then he will be able to divert his attention from the symptom and fix it upon the actual underlying fault.

In the case of the boy mentioned above, we saw that the priest gave him advice in this sense. But, at this point, we must draw attention to a difficulty that crops up again and again in dealing with self-abuse. The onanist is usually insecure in his spiritual life and tends to withdraw unto himself to seek security. The more such a subject is under the influence of his bad habit, the more difficult he will find it not to drag the self-abuse into the distraction itself. He will think: " I must occupy myself in this or that manner in order to distract my mind from self-abuse." What does this " in order to " mean, if not that the mind is *still* occupied with self-abuse? It is not truly distracted. This emerged from the words used by the boy himself. Thus we perceive how vitally important it is to deprive the habit of its weight as a deadly sin and put it in its true position as a *symptom.* Then the patient will learn, gradually, to look upon it as no more than an alarm signal reminding him that all is not yet well with his attitude to life. Should he continue with his bad habit, he will say to himself: " Ah ! there you see that you are still too weak ; you have not yet learned to turn your forces in the right direction. You must do more to fulfil your life-tasks, for yourself and for others."

Let us take up the second point (b). It is not as a rule very difficult to point out to an onanist the real underlying causes of his addiction. We have to ask ourselves, and to ask him, what it is that he is in actual reality looking for. In the case of the little Hans it is clear enough : he was looking for the love and tenderness which he had sought for in vain from his mother. Not getting it where he should rightly have received it, he turned to himself and sought for satisfaction in that way.

That the result, namely self-abuse, gave him no true satisfaction we need hardly say. To ask: " Did you then finally find the satisfaction you sought? " is, in most cases, to receive from an onanist the answer—certainly not !

This chain of cause and effect must be made as clear as possible to the penitent, so that he can say: " I am looking for something right in itself but missing in my life. I try to find this in myself ; but this self-love can never replace real love for another, so the pleasure I get is without genuine satisfaction. It is clear that I am on the wrong road. It remains for me to discover the *right* road, along which real satisfaction and fulfilment is to be found. Further, I am not now a child seeking passively to receive love, tenderness or pleasure ; and I know that real satisfaction and higher fulfilment will come to me only when I become active and creative and learn to give." Self-abuse is a childish thing, a form of regress-ion, when it persists in later life ; a child does not know how to give ; that comes later in life when childhood is transcended.

Then comes the quest for *a new purpose*, bringing fulfilment. Here those who seek to help the penitent can be of great use. The main thing is to turn the mind and body towards new interests, to distract the penitent from his self-absorption. These interests should provide joy and satisfaction. Youth movements and groups of all sorts for sport, travel, walks, etc., will be of value.

The onanist who finds the right way into a fuller life will make his own ex-perience. The more he throws himself into the new life, the more free and joyful he will become, and the problem of self-abuse will sink into the background. It is true that his habit may return. There may be difficulties and set-backs. This must be taken as a signal that he has not thrown himself sufficiently into his fuller life.

To turn to the third point (c) : all this might not have proved adequate for our little boy Hans. His mother stood for his " world," and this factor cannot be ignored, especially in the case of younger children ; the outward influences then assume greater significance. Bodies appointed to give advice to parents can play a part in all such cases. We know well that the mothers often need help and advice more than do the children ! It is very necessary to hold serious talks with the mothers, with a view to the correction of faults in education and even more to aid in the revision, when needful, of their entire attitude towards their children. As a woman's attitude to her child is apt to reflect her general life-outlook, talks of this kind are excellent pointers in the spiritual care of the parents. The possibilities of influencing parents through their children are important and well known to the educator.

(February, 1951)

TREATMENT OF SELF-ABUSE IN BOYS
by ALOIS GÜGLER

This contribution represents the last chapter of a book by Gügler entitled : *Die Erziehliche Behandlung jugendlicher männlicher Onanisten.*

THE LITERATURE of this subject must be studied in a highly critical spirit. In pedagogy in general an over-emphasis laid upon any special science or branch of science leads, of necessity, to unjustifiable generalisations, to the laying down of laws based upon inadequate foundations. In so-called sexual pedagogy the same observation holds good, more especially in relation to the problem of self-abuse. It is essential to hold closely to the formal principles of pedagogy, and to avoid trespassing upon the ground of other disciplines, while allowing these to enjoy their rightful influences. It is in this way alone that we can obtain the conditions vital to educational success, and guard against half-measures that may do more harm than good.

The right outlook on the problem of self-abuse is to be obtained only by means of a wide psychological pedagogical review, fully taking into account all the various phases of development. Such an outlook will teach us that self-abuse is not to be regarded as a separate phenomenon, and that its real significance is to be sought in its character as a symptom. The sexual organs and their functions, including the orgasm, are means of expression. Since self-abuse, more readily than any other form of sexual expression, is available at any time, it can be a symptom of every conceivable mode of experience and will have its own form for each individual, according to his disposition and upbringing. Accordingly, we may say that self-abuse, at least in its more developed forms, is a means of " shaping a situation " (*Situations-gestaltung*).

A more detailed analysis of the habit in regard to age, basic character, and type of practice, leads us to the highly important conclusion that the occasional and temporary self-abuse of puberty—conditioned by awakening sexual urges as well as by psychic factors—is a developmental phenomenon and need not cause us special anxiety or lead to over-much concern as to preventive steps. It is quite a different matter, however, with excessive self-abuse, either *before* or *after* the time of puberty.

A consideration of the different dispositions and conditions which can be held responsible for this habit and can promote the act of self-abuse makes it quite clear that the educational treatment of those in question is no more than a *part* of the general educational problem and can be tackled with success only within the framework of the whole personality.

We cannot assume direct results as following from the practice ; but the psychic consequences are the commonest and the most important of the indirect results. These often follow upon the mistaken attitude of those who form the personal environment of the subect.

Since self-abuse is a symptom, it follows that there is not and cannot be an isolated educational treatment. It is always a case of cleaning up the breeding ground upon which the practice flourishes ; and, when the practice is chronic and excessive, this includes a complete bodily and spiritual re-education of the personality with, in many cases, appropriate medical aid. The educational treatment requires a relationship of strong confidence and a careful study of the psychological make-up and modes of reaction of the individual. In the periods of late and post-puberty (and, in a few cases, earlier), an analysis of the phantasies which accompany the sexual feelings of the subject may yield valuable pointers as to the psychic tendencies and dominant urges of the subject. The three main aims in the education of onanists, which are closely linked together, are: self-confidence, consciousness of success, and joy. What the subject needs is to be liberated from the continual depression of his situation, to know, through his own experience, that he can successfully overcome his trouble, and to recover the joys of self-satisfaction and self-confidence. The one-sided and so often psychopathic self-love of these cases one can seek to overcome through a re-awakening of love and devotion directed towards another person.

This process of spiritual healing depends upon the elimination of the factors making for self-abuse, whether these are direct or indirect, objective or personal. A hardening of the body by means of systematic exercises will help to make it less sensitive ; but with these physical means the decisive thing is the mental reaction. The control of phantasy is an essential condition for a successful educational treatment and this is best brought about when mind and body are taken up with interesting activities bringing joy with them ; in their absence a cure is hardly thinkable. The whole of this educational process must rest upon a foundation of powerful *motives*. The subjective values of the individual should be taken into due consideration. but we must never cease to place before him motives of a dynamic character, strengthened and confirmed by wise guidance. These should be, to a much larger extent than has often been the case hitherto, of a *social* and not merely individual character.

The *prophylaxis* includes all the reasonable demands of a responsible *hygiene*, as well as those of a well-balanced *general education* in a favourable environment. Initiation into the nature and meaning of the physical and psychic experiences of puberty should be taken by degrees and be accompanied by the encouragement of a healthy self-respect and self-valuation and an all-round character training, finding its central purpose in a firmly established, noble, and inspiring ideal of life ; in this fashion we can best ward off the danger of chronic self-abuse, as far as this is possible within the limits laid down by heredity.

In conclusion, we must repeat that the problem of self-abuse can be solved only in the light of the development of personality as a whole ; this is the only safe method, as regards both protection and cure, and the best method of safeguarding the educator himself from becoming " fixed " upon the sexual aspect of life. We should like to conclude by quoting L. Hansel: " There is just as little and just as much purity in the world as there is real honesty, real justice and real love. If there were more of these things there would be more purity."

(*June,* 1951)

THE MORAL AND RELIGIOUS GUILT OF THE ACT OF SELF-ABUSE

by Heinz Fleckenstein
Professor of Moral Theology, Würzburg

THE AUTHOR of this article does not seek to extend or supplement the valuable ideas that have been put before the readers of *Katechetische Blätter* by the moral theologian Angermair, and the psychotherapists von Gebsattel, von Gagern and A. Gügler : this would take him beyond his proper competence. It is his aim to integrate the (in part) new viewpoints of doctors and psychologists with the timeless and unchanging principles of moral and pastoral theology and, at the same time, to advance certain rules helpful in the priestly treatment of those suffering from self-abuse.

1. Let us begin by saying that both moral and pastoral theology, with the practical care of souls, are willing gratefully to accept findings and advice from medical and psychological quarters. This applies, in general, to questions concerning the evaluation and treatment of spiritual disorders and, more especially, to our present problem.

(a) It should indeed be even more freely and emphatically recognised in theological science and in the care of souls that psychotherapists have *a decisive word to say* as to the moral guilt and general treatment of disordered persons, with special reference to the evaluation of moral blame. It cannot be denied that there are to-day not a few cases of habitual self-abuse with a strong character of compulsion. For decades we have heard from scientific and practical quarters of " compulsory onanaism " or " self-abuse under compulsion " and in some cases there is no question of any pleasure being derived (see. Rh. Liertz). Further investigation seems to point to the fact that we have to do, largely, with so-called " secondary compulsory acts." States of suppression and of anxiety create and increase conditions making for false manifestations of life, to a point at which, in some cases, the moral responsibility for practices in themselves gravely sinful may be looked upon as virtually non-existent.

Christian psychotherapists—Catholics in particular—do not go beyond their proper sphere when they venture to say that, in states of anxiety and obsession, actions may be performed of a nature so complicated that they must *seem* to be the result of consideration and free will yet are not: and, accordingly, such actions are " devoid of every—I repeat *every*—serious element of guilt " (W. Bergmann) ; and that often the judgment of self-abuse as solely a moral problem is an error (von Gagern). They are justified, also, in demanding that, in the care of souls, the multiplication of psychic disorders in the present day should be taken into account, and with it the increased number of cases of self-abuse in which it may be regarded and treated as not so much a sin (or at least a sin alone) as a symptom of general maladjustment of life and its demands. They even have the right to demand from priests that they should not endanger the healing of such moral disorders by an objectively unjustifiable pedagogy grounded in fear, or by increasing anxieties caused by feelings of sin and guilt ; but should, on the contrary, help to make the curative process possible, by removing an objectively unjustifiable fear of sin.

Moral theology has long been aware that nervous disorders have increased and that in cases where there is resistance in mind and will no mortal sin—and not seldom no sin of any kind—is to be found. Pastoral practice, however, has been in many cases too slow to draw the necessary practical lessons.

(b) Starting with the study of diseased cases, psychotherapists have learned many things which are of vital significance not only for " border-cases," but also for those who are quite normal. It is a fruitful and happy methodical principle of modern medical psychology—and of other branches of science — to make use of the distortions and caricatures of diseased states to advance the knowledge of the normal, which contains in lesser and often barely perceptible measure the same factors so much more easily perceived when exaggerated by disease. Onanism—that is to say, the firmly established practice of self-abuse, in later life, as distinct from isolated acts of temporary habits in puberty—is always something more than a " normal " concern. It is, in reality, in every case " also a symptom," as the psychotherapists say. We can only be grateful if the study of onanism can give us pointers in the treatment and judgment of normal (often only apparently normal) cases. Above all, psychotherapy can provide us with guidance in the matter of prevention and the avoidance of errors, especially those due to false educational measures, thus enabling us to help parents and others in charge of young children to act more wisely. The psychotherapeutical principle (see for example von Gagern) that, in dealing with self-abuse amongst children, the parents require treatment side-by-side with their children is as right as it is important. That serious educational blunders are often responsible for the beginning or the abnormal further development of bad habits is a sad fact, but one that can sometimes be avoided by appropriate guidance. The rule that anything likely to discourage the young person in this field is always dangerous and false is to be accepted ; also the warning against every sort of moral over-severity.

2. It is a matter-of-course that, while practical theology and spiritual direction willingly consider the findings and suggestions of science and medicine, there can never be the slightest question of any surrender or even modification of *the principles of moral theology*. It might be worth while, however, to consider seriously whether the *current application* of these principles should not be subjected to examination.

(a) The principles can be outlined briefly as follows: Objectively considered, it is certain that self-abuse is an act contrary to the order of nature, an offence against the essential nature of the sexual act designed as a bi-personal act of love, rendering possible the continuation of the race. The union of two persons of opposite sexes is an essential part of the act and the pleasure attached to it. On the other hand, the act of self-abuse, even when performed with the body of another person, male or female, as an instrument, is a solitary act and a breach of normal social contacts (Angermair). Self-abuse signifies not only isolation in a personal sense but, at the same time, an isolation of a part of the sexual act, that which provides pleasure, from the act as a whole, with its natural meaning and purpose. (Duland has defined unchastity with precision as, in its essence, the " separation of pleasure from duty.") It is very obvious that this kind of sexual activity contradicts the essential order linking sexuality and propagation—and for this reason it ranks as *actus contra naturam*.

Thus we may say that this act introduces confusion into the order designed by God (Angermair). It is, accordingly, a perversion envisaged objectively from the moral-theological standpoint, apart altogether from the disputed question as to whether it must be regarded as perverse or unnatural from the quite different standpoint of *medical* normality (in the sense of the state of the subject and his psychopathic condition: see Gebsattel). The Scripture and official teaching of the Church support the natural arguments of moral theology (for example, the mentioning of the *molles* as sinners (Cor. 6 : 9). See also the rejection by Innocent XI of the saying that self-abuse is not forbidden by nature (p.d. 49. D 1119), as well as the statement of the Holy Office of August 2, 1929.

If the pleasure attached to the specific excitement of the organs and functions proper to propagation is consciously sought after outside legitimate marriage, whether as means or end, and is directly and freely willed, modern theologians are in agreement that it comes under the head of *delectatio venerea in se volita seu directe quaesita non admittit paritatem matrriae*. Thus every action outside marriage that has for its purpose, objectively, the obtaining of sexual satisfaction and, subjectively, is thus sought freely and consciously is not only, from the natural standpoint, a grave sin, but is a mortal sin from the standpoint of personal guilt and moral responsibility. When the Holy Office (Aug. 2, 1929) specifically declared that even the preservation of health does not justify the direct bringing about of a pollution,* that not only self-abuse for its own sake, but the act done for another purpose is reckoned as a mortal sin if done with consent and free will. A pollution which arises from a state of excitation is not directly willed ; if an act has as its object some purpose other than sexual satisfaction or excitement and considered subjectively is directed towards this other purpose, the act can be carried out, given serious cause, without sin or at least without grave sin—in as far as there is no danger of the acts, taking place with consent.

(*b*) When these immovable principles are considered in relation to the complexities of life and the teachings of psychotherapy in particular, we arrive at three essential categories of cases.

Firstly, we can speak of self-abuse in the proper sense only if a state of sexual excitement *is sought after*—otherwise the knowledge vital to the concept of mortal sin is not present.

In the case of the merely playful pleasure-seeking acts of small children, a vague not specifically sexual purpose is the decisive factor, as we shall expect from the character of life at that age. In early puberty, too, such acts can take place without the pleasure sought after being experienced as something specifically sexual, differentiated from the joy of the senses in general. For this reason, doctors and psychologists speak of "practices akin to self-abuse," " pseudo-onanistic practices," etc. But, in the case of persons who are more or less normal, there results sooner or later, perhaps gradually, perhaps suddenly, a knowledge of the specifically sexual nature of the pleasure. Conscience begins to assert itself and feelings of guilt become active. It is clear that if sexual pleasure, in the specific sense, is *not* sought after, there cannot be either grave sin in the objective sense or mortal sin the subjective sense. But in individual cases where we have a more or less uneasy state of conscience, it is quite possible for venial sin to occur.

Secondly, an act of self-abuse, even when consciously directed to sexual pleasure, is not always *a free act*: that is to say, the sexual satisfaction, even though sought after directly, is not always and in every case *freely* willed, so that what is objectively a grave sin is often, owing to the lack of true freedom, not a mortal sin in the sense of personal guilt and subjective responsibility. The freedom necessary to establish mortal sin is lacking. We certainly cannot accept the somewhat weak excuses (referred to by Angermair) ; but it is necessary to recognise the genuine inhibitions and limitations of freedom in order that conscience should not be over-burdened and the easy-going and unscrupulous be encouraged in laxity, while good sensitive types are exposed to conscientious scruples, causing anxiety and serious spiritual conflicts, possibly leading to neurotic dangers.

*This is not an answer to the question of principle : is such a case possible in itself ? It deals solely with the question: if such an extreme case should arise, according to the opinion of the subject, such a direct bringing about cannot be regarded as a permitted choice. *A fortiori* it is an answer, and a negative one, to the question put by doctors : is it permissible, in the case of a fertility test, to obtain the needful semen from the husband by means of self-abuse ?

If we have a bad habit carried forward from the days of early childhood or early puberty, but not in itself to be regarded as a mortal sin (owing to reasons connected with lack of moral knowledge, being led astray at an early age, or general corrupting influences), some ground of excuse must be found, for the same reasons, in the case of similar acts of a later date. As Angermair points out, we have here a discrepancy between the strength of the will and that of the over-stimulated lower urges. This excuse should not be held valid for too long a period, unless there are special factors in the subject's life history which place a too heavy burden on the will, and exaggerate the intensity of the instinctive urges to a point far beyond the normal. Together with bad early influences and defects of disposition, the mistakes of an erroneous type of education play a sad role (for example, the sharp punishment of practices akin to self-abuse, as described by von Gagern). In such cases—and they are not rare—there exists, at least for a time, a " de-compensation " of the power of moral resistance, for which the subject is not, at least not directly, responsible ; this liberates the individual act, during the time of puberty and of early maturity, from the stigma of grave guilt—but this does not mean, of necessity, from all guilt.

When we consider the later ages, when maturity should have been achieved, only the genuinely pathological cases can be looked upon, in general, as free from grave guilt. That these cases do exist and that they are now more common than previously has often enough been commented upon by doctors, theologians, psychotherapists and priests—although not all priests are sufficiently aware of this ! Hence these articles in the present periodical. A study of the life-history of the individual is usually sufficient to make it clear that we are dealing with a case of disorder. We have already pointed out that the doctor should say something decisive to the priest in such cases. It will very often be the duty of the priest to be the first to inform the subject that his actual state is one of illness and direct him to a Christian psychotherapist who will understand him, if the priest is not himself successful in enabling the penitent to grasp his own state and if the abnormality is so serious that it cannot be dealt with by priestly aid alone. (This applies to most serious cases, so that the priest would not go far wrong in sending all such cases to a suitable doctor.)

The most essential curative work to be done by a priest in this type of case is the removal, or at least the diminution, of anxiety as to sin, and this can usually be accomplished by suggesting with conviction that, in such a case, no serious burden of guilt need rest upon the conscience. What we have here is an inability to fight successfully against the habit, after long exhausting struggles, with strong resistance from the will and emotional centres. That, in such cases, no mortal sin (to say the least) is present, either in the habit or each act, is the certain opinion of all writers on moral theology. Further, experienced theologians (see Eberle) lend their support to psychotherapists in asserting that liberation from the fear of mortal sin is a condition of bringing about a cure. It is the fear of temptation and another fall—so sinful in their eyes—which, more than anything else, calls forth continual states of inward tension and anxiety and these in their turn, as Eberle puts it, drive the subject to further practices to relieve the tension. Psychology has undoubtedly shown in no uncertain fashion that onanism plays a large part as a means of reaction against feelings of inferiority, as a protest against a life that has not been mastered, as a self-isolation against the claims of a social life that is beyond the capacity of the subject to deal with, especially in cases of duo-sexuality. These individuals know themselves that they are most likely to suffer reverses when discouraged, disappointed or, in general, when depressed ; and those who can observe themselves know that that they are at their weakest when driven back upon themselves, or still more when they have suppressed, or sought to suppress, depressing experiences. It is clear that self-abuse is something more than an unmistakable disturbance of the sexual order ; it is, as von Gagern emphasises, a *signal of alarm* to tell us that something is radically wrong in our life-attitude. The guilt lies deeper down and further back ! Acts of self-abuse of this kind, a source of torment rather than pleasure, practised more against the will than with consent, are without a doubt free from grievous sin—although we cannot say in advance and in every case that they are wholly without guilt, for amongst the contributory causes there must be many not free from blameworthy weakness. We cannot agree, however, with the priests quoted by von Gagern who say, with what we regard as premature bluntness, that, " it is not a sin but an illness," for we feel that the position should not be over-simplified. It is not a mere " either-or," for its complexity demands a much less simple formula, say perhaps " this—and also that ! "

In the **third** place, the *understanding* and *free will* proper to grave guilt are, on the other hand, to be presumed in the case of *adult* onanists, unless there are unmistakable signs of a general inability for adjustment to adult life. Persons of an introspective type are apt to fall into this class ; they always want to over-come bad habits, but owing to wrong methods of fighting and overanxiety always sink back again ; on the other hand, those of a robust, vital, and extro-verted type tend, when fully mature and at their highest level of vitality, to a lax mode of life more especially in the field of sex. These hardened sinners must not, out of regard for the former class, be treated with a quite unsuitable degree of mildness, and should not be allowed to " get away with " the excuses they may put forward. Such types are only too apt to slide back into their bad habits and become ever more difficult to help. Despite good intentions, made from time to time, they do not try hard *enough*—often they only half try—to break away from their habits ; and they are inclined to produce all sorts of thin excuses and expect, and even demand, recognition of these by the confessor. Such types are only too likely to slip down further and further and end by becoming truly vicious. We must not forget that in these mature cases we can expect understanding and, unless the abuse is altogether excessive, free will. Even if we were to assume that the individual act, owing to the force of long established custom, is to be looked upon as free of grave guilt, the fact that the self-abuse is so established is often in itself a grave sin, since it is an expression of a lack of moral conscientiousness and of an earnest desire to master life. This attitude is often the way to an " insincere conscience " ; the penitent pretends to himself that " it's not so bad after all " and manufactures all sorts of more or less feeble excuses. Weakness of will and the *ignorantia culpabilis* which may ensue cannot be allowed as genuine extenuating circumstances. A drying up of the moral and religious life in general usually lies at the end of this downward path ; sins are absorbed as if they were water, without any heart-felt disturbance of the conscience and ensuing true repentance. Such penitents will slip away from the priests' hands more and more. All the more grave is the responsibility of the confessor who may have to deal with them on some special occasion, such as Easter, marriage, or grave illness, It will be his duty to impress upon the penitent with all possible earnestness the grave nature of his sin and the danger in a continuance of his way of life.

This vital extroverted type plays a smaller part in the discussion of self-abuse than that allotted to the less vital, more introspective type. There are two reasons for this. Firstly, such persons are much more likely to find their way to natural sexual relationships, although they may be far from keeping to the laws of God in this field. Secondly, they do not often find their way to the consulting room of the psychotherapist and are not so much in the habit of appealing to a priest for aid.

3.   The following pointers, useful in the spiritual treatment of self-abuse, can be highlighted from the foregoing material :

(a) Each *individual case* must be considered specifically as to its characteristics and life-history. The priest, and more especially the confessor, must know about the beginnings of the practice and understand the moral type with its development, its success and failures, and have some know-ledge of the chief difficulties of the penitent, both interior and exterior. This must be done before a judgment worthy of his responsible office can be formed, wise guidance be given, and the penitent be aided to set himself reasonable aims and form wise resolutions. At least at the beginning of the treatment, there must be a thorough discussion of the position. Even in the case of the penitent who comes once only, the priest must seek, by means of a few well chosen questions (put in the tone of one who wishes above all to help), to relate the present confession to previous ones, in order to compare the position in respect of this particular trouble. A better education in confession during the adolescent years would be of value in helping the penitent to make the needful explanation to a new confessor.

(b) The *existence of mortal sin* must not be presumed as a matter-of-course, in complaints as to self-abuse. *This still happens too readily.* All guidance in matters of sex must keep to the "middle of the road" and avoid the two extremes of being easy going and too fanatical. The judgment of each particular case must not be too lax, prematurely hastening to forgive and to explain that there can be no mortal sin, or even no sin at all ; and not too rigorous, looking for sin everywhere and admitting extenuating circumstances only with the utmost reluctance. And, as we have said, when a case is definitely recognisable as one of real disorder or illness, the priest must do his best to relieve the exaggerated sense of guilt. In some cases he may have to awaken the feeling, in a particular case, that it is more a question of illness than of sin ; otherwise the habit may prove intractable, neurotic degeneration may set in, or we may get an obstinate attitude of laxity or a deliberate plunging into degradation. In such a case the liberation from a sense of sin takes place in order to promote moral health. The care of souls in the Church has always insisted upon evidence in the case of mortal sins alleged to have been committed by over-scrupulous neurotics. Recent knowledge tends to support this view and carries the responsibility of the confessor still further. We must admit that, in the case of self-abuse conditioned by purpose, the existence of mortal sin is more readily to be presumed than when the act is causal in origin. But in both cases the true nature of the excuse must be proven.

(e) When it has become well established for priest or penitent that a *mortal sin does not exist* in the case in view, that does *not* exclude a lesser degree of guilt. An exception is the case of genuine illness, when actions are done under compulsion by victims of obsessional neurosis. Both medicine and jurisprudence warn us against regarding psychopathic persons as being automatically free of *all* responsibility. In this way we not only deprive them of human dignity but we may take away from them the last re-straining influences. It is true that they have a lesser degree of respon-sibility, so that they cannot as a rule be charged with mortal sin. But that does not exclude the possibility of a venial sin in certain cases. Moreover, let us not forget that the subject may well be more or less guilty in respect of his own state looking into the past ; guilt might be discovered—possibly guilt of a *different* sort. This may be the origin of the disorder which later emerged in the sexual field.

(d) *Wise care for the future*, the aiding of the penitent in regaining self-confidence and good will and forming good resolutions is more impor-tant than the giving of a verdict at any price. For this reason, the con-fessor may quite well, at least sometimes, leave the final decision as to whether or not mortal sin is present to Him who searches the depth of the heart, more especially if he feels that genuine repentance and an honest intention to overcome evil are present. At the same time, he will have sometimes to check a too rosy view of the situation, an over-confident belief that now all will be well, and to point out, cautiously, that there is always the possiblity of another fall, accompanying this with a firm injunction to endure this, with its shame and humiliation, should it occur, with due patience and to rise again and continue the struggle without delay. Moral and pastoral theologians often regard a diminution in the number of falls, in the case of long habituated sinners, as an indication of good will. The priest must avoid the danger that the penitent gives up his struggle after a fall and adopts a mood of resignation, thinking that, in his case, despite good will there is really " nothing to be done." It is highly important to lead the penitent to form right and possible resolutions. The main factors in resolutions will be an energetic positive application of the penitent's powers* rather than with any *direct* struggle against the evil itself. In most cases this is the right method, and it is the most effective in severe cases. The doctor should be able to help the priest with valuable hints.

(e) *We must carefully avoid causing discouragement.* We repeat, with the utmost emphasis, our warning of the danger of the old-style pedagogy of striking terror into victims of self-abuse. Almost every Christian psychotherapist and many priests can tell of cases where acute neurosis followed upon shock caused by horrific tales of the consequences of the " secret sin " (including usually, even to-day, accounts of spinal paralysis, etc.), derived perhaps from some mission lecture or from ultra-rigorous methods employed in the confessional. It has long been clearly established that serious physical injury may possibly result from excessive addiction to the practice during puberty, but hardly in any other way. On the other hand, the danger of a fixation of attention upon sexual matters due to fear is very real. Thus the power of resistance is undermined and the young person handed over to the grip of the habit. There is the further danger that an individual who has been trained through fear of outward punishment in this field will fling over the traces when he discovers that the fear is exaggerated, or perhaps because some non-Christian doctor influences him, and the end result will be a total loss of all control in sexual matters. In not a few cases, a complete loss of religious faith has come about through the belief that the teaching religion must be as false on *other* points as it has been found to be on *this* one ! It is thus essential to dig much deeper down in order to arouse the right kind of feeling for what is wrong in this field, while at the same time strengthening, by every means, natural and supernatural, the conviction that every individual can secure his salvation through the all-pervading grace of God, providing that his will is turned in the right direction, even though it may not be a strong will. Only through this *confidence* can the will be built up and finally become capable of overcoming even an old-established habit.

We priests should seek to deepen more and more our consciousness of the heavy responsibility of the care of souls and of the confessional in particular, and should always make a special point of the most serious prayer for divine wisdom before the hearing of confessions. And not least we should frequently remind the faithful to pray for the gift of good confessors. Perhaps that is one of the most important tasks of the day of the priestly office ?

---

*The following points suggest themselves : practice in social feeling ; improvement of relationships inward and outward—to relations and others ; deepening of interior life in prayer and the sacraments ; greater conscientiousness in professional life ; systematic employment of spare time, physical gardening, and training of the body.